THINKING SKILLS FOR work

Phil Freeman

Acknowledgements:
George Panther for video direction and magic.
Simon Hammond for video production.
Jayne Garner for editing.
Actors: Kevin Collins, Josh Mumby, Natalie Russo, Vicky Wujeratne from Liverpool Theatre School.

ISBN 978-1-84618-189-4
Axis Education
PO Box 459
Shrewsbury SY4 4WZ
Email:enquiries@axiseducation.co.uk
www.axiseducation.co.uk

First published 2009

Contents

Contents

General introduction

AIMS

- to develop listening and observational skills, oral and written communication skills, all of which are related to the world of work
- to develop a variety of basic functional skills
- to develop these skills within the PLTS (Personal, Learning and Thinking Skills) framework, encouraging pupils to become independent enquirers, creative thinkers, reflective learners, team workers and self-managers.

THEMES COVERED

We have grouped the activities within this title so that they relate to different aspects of work:

- Getting a job/wages
- Training
- On the job
- Customer care
- Work problems and relationships.

(See contents page for worksheet titles.)

Each exercise contains activities for students and suggestions for extension activities, together with stimulus materials in a variety of forms including:

- written text and/or drawings
- audio clips
- video clips.

Each exercise contains sufficient material for a one-hour lesson.

There are also teacher's notes, answers, and mapping documents for each exercise at the back of the book, along with an assessment and evaluation document for students to fill in at the end of the programme of study.

HOW TO USE THIS BOOK

With exercises based on written text we suggest that you adopt one of two approaches depending on the abilities of your students and your targets for their learning:

- ask students to read the text themselves
- ask students to listen to the text read aloud by an appropriate person.

For exercises based on audio clips or video clips students will need access to computers or an interactive white board. You should use your discretion in allowing students to re-play the audio clips and video clips. The number of times they do this will depend on the complexity of the activity and the ability of the students.

General introduction

In every exercise students should be encouraged to make notes whilst reading, listening to or watching the stimulus material. Written answers can be handwritten or word-processed. Whenever possible, you should allow students to carry out research on the internet. Most of the exercises can be carried out either by students working alone or in small groups. In some cases there is a recommendation that one of these two options would be more appropriate but in other cases the choice can be made by the teacher, based on the abilities of the students and the targets for their learning.

The skills developed will relate to the world of work but will also have relevance to all areas of the curriculum. However, some exercises will relate more specifically to particular subject areas. These are highlighted in the Teacher's notes.

PLTS FRAMEWORK

The table on pages 7–8 shows the main areas of the PLTS framework covered in each individual activity. By completing all of the exercises, every area of the PLTS framework will be covered.

General introduction

Exercises	Independent enquirers						Creative thinkers						Reflective learners						Team workers						Self managers						Effective participators					
	A	B	C	D	E	F	A	B	C	D	E	F	A	B	C	D	E	F	A	B	C	D	E	F	A	B	C	D	E	F	A	B	C	D	E	F
Jobs 1																																				
Jobs 2																																				
Interview 1	*	*		*	*	*		*		*			*					*	*	*	*	*	*	*		*						*		*	*	
Interview 2	*	*		*	*	*		*		*			*					*	*	*	*	*	*	*		*						*		*	*	
Interview 3	*	*		*	*	*		*		*		*	*				*	*	*	*	*	*	*	*		*						*		*	*	
Just the job?																																				
Wages																																				
A fair wage?	*		*	*			*	*	*	*	*	*				*		*	*	*			*			*	*								*	*
Talking	*		*	*	*	*	*	*	*	*				*		*			*	*		*	*	*		*	*					*			*	*
Literacy levels at work	*		*	*		*	*	*	*	*	*			*	*	*		*	*	*	*	*	*	*		*	*				*	*	*	*	*	
Magic	*	*		*		*	*	*	*	*	*	*	*		*	*	*	*	*	*	*		*	*		*						*	*		*	*
Menu	*			*			*				*		*	*	*		*	*				*	*	*	*	*	*									
Following Instructions – know your napkins	*			*		*	*	*	*	*	*	*	*	*	*	*	*	*							*	*	*				*	*	*	*	*	
Following instructions – serviette style	*			*		*	*	*	*	*	*	*	*	*	*	*	*	*	*	*	*	*	*	*	*	*	*				*	*	*	*	*	
Darts	*		*	*			*	*			*	*	*	*		*	*	*	*	*		*	*	*		*	*						*	*	*	*
Introducing Z Factor																																				
Finish the lyrics																																				
Breaking news																																				
News headlines	*			*			*	*	*		*	*	*		*	*	*	*	*	*	*	*	*	*		*	*				*	*	*	*	*	
Picture this																																				
Picture that																																				
Picture these																																				

General introduction

Exercises	Independent enquirers						Creative thinkers						Reflective learners						Team workers						Self managers						Effective participators					
	A	B	C	D	E	F	A	B	C	D	E	F	A	B	C	D	E	F	A	B	C	D	E	F	A	B	C	D	E	F	A	B	C	D	E	F
The Daily Blag																																				
Pedalo power	*		*			*	*	*	*		*	*	*	*		*	*	*	*	*	*	*	*	*	*	*	*				*	*	*	*	*	*
The fishing line	*		*	*		*	*	*	*	*	*		*	*	*	*	*	*	*	*	*	*	*	*		*	*					*	*	*	*	*
Public speaking	*		*	*		*	*	*	*	*			*	*		*	*	*	*	*	*	*	*	*		*	*					*	*	*	*	
Speaking in public																																				
Listen carefully	*	*		*		*	*	*	*		*		*	*	*	*	*	*			*	*	*			*		*					*	*	*	
Customer care 1			*	*		*	*		*		*					*			*	*			*	*		*					*	*	*	*		
Customer care 2			*	*		*	*		*		*					*			*	*			*	*		*					*	*	*	*		
Customer care 3																																				
Phone calls	*		*	*		*	*	*	*		*		*	*		*	*	*	*	*		*	*	*		*						*	*	*	*	
Satisfied customers	*		*	*		*	*	*	*	*	*			*		*		*	*	*		*	*	*		*	*					*	*	*	*	
Help!	*			*		*	*	*	*	*	*	*	*		*	*	*	*	*	*	*	*	*	*		*						*		*	*	
The boss blunders																																				
A phone call from the boss	*		*	*		*	*	*			*	*	*		*	*	*		*	*	*		*	*	*	*	*				*	*	*	*	*	
When things go wrong																																				
Eyewitness	*			*		*	*	*	*	*	*		*			*	*	*	*	*	*	*	*	*		*						*		*	*	
Every picture tells a story	*		*	*	*	*	*	*	*	*	*	*				*		*	*	*		*	*	*		*	*								*	
Body language 1	*		*	*	*	*	*	*	*	*	*					*		*	*	*		*	*	*		*	*								*	
Body language 2	*		*	*	*	*	*	*	*	*	*					*		*	*	*		*	*	*		*	*								*	*
Stranded	*		*	*	*	*	*	*	*	*	*	*	*	*		*		*	*	*	*	*	*	*	*	*	*	*			*	*	*	*	*	

Jobs 1

Read these job advertisements from The Gurnsley Echo.

1.

The **Latvian State Circus** has vacancies for the following positions:

- Human Cannon Ball
- Fire-Eater
- Clown
- Juggler

No experience necessary. On-the-job training will be provided. Generous living allowance. Clothing provided. Free life insurance. £12,000 pa.

**The Latvian State Circus is an Equal Opportunities employer and welcomes applicants of all ages, religious and ethnic backgrounds, including those with disabilities.

2.

Pauline's Poodle Parlour

Dog trimmer required for part-time work, three days per week initially, in this exclusive city-centre establishment. Previous experience an advantage but not essential. Excellent working conditions. Overalls provided. Applicants must have good communication skills. £6.50 per hour.

3.

Casey's Key Cutters

Assistant key cutter required to cover for maternity leave. This temporary position in a small family-run business requires a person with good hand-eye coordination and an affinity with machinery. Candidates should have BTEC in Advanced Key Cutting or equivalent. Opportunity for position to be made permanent dependent on performance.

Starting salary £240 pw.

4.

Dingley's Department Store

We require a team of elves to work in Santa's Grotto this Christmas. This is an opportunity for anyone hoping to break into show-business.

Applicants will be expected to sing, dance and talk to young children. As part of our policy of positive discrimination, we welcome applications from senior citizens.

One week induction period, during which training will be provided.

Season begins 1 September and ends 24 December.

Elves will be expected to work a six-day, two-shift system, alternating each week, and be prepared to cover for absent colleagues when requested to do so.

Daily rate £8 per hour for eight-hour shift.

Free visits to the Grotto for immediate family members.

*Please include recent photograph with application.

Answer these questions on your own.

The Latvian State Circus

▶ 1. What is 'on-the-job training'?

....

▶ 2. Why is free life insurance provided?

....

Jobs 1

▶ 3. Approximately how much would you earn per week in these jobs?

▶ 4. Although the Latvian State Circus is 'an Equal Opportunities' employer, would there be any people who might not be able to do these jobs?

▶ 5. What do the letters 'CV' stand for?

Pauline's Poodle Parlour

▶ 6. What is meant by three days per week 'initially'?

▶ 7. This job involves working with dogs. Why do you need 'good communication skills'?

▶ 8. If you worked eight hours a day for three days how much would you earn in this job?

▶ 9. What is a 'CV'?

Casey's Key Cutters

▶ 10. What is meant by 'cover for maternity leave'?

▶ 11. What is an 'affinity'?

▶ 12. What is 'good hand-eye coordination' and why is it necessary?

▶ 13. What is meant by 'opportunity for position to be made permanent dependent on performance'?

▶ 14. What is the approximate annual salary?

Jobs 1

Dingley's Department Store

▶ 15. What does 'positive discrimination' mean?

▶ 16. Who are 'senior citizens'?

▶ 17. What is an 'induction period'?

▶ 18. What does 'six day, two-shift system, alternating each week' mean?

▶ 19. How much would you earn each day in this job?

▶ 20. What is one of the 'perks' of this job?

▶ 21. Why does your application need to include a recent photograph?

▶ 22. From the four jobs, choose the one you would most like to apply for. Give reasons for your choice.

Jobs 2

On the previous worksheets you looked at four jobs that were advertised in The Gurnsley Echo. The jobs were at:

- ***The Latvian State Circus***
- ***Pauline's Poodle Parlour***
- ***Casey's Key Cutters***
- ***Dingley's Department Store***

Here is a letter of application that was received by Pauline's Poodle Parlour.

Flat 12
Varley Court
Gurnsley
GY7 3DL

13 September

Dear Pauline

I would like to apply for the job of Dog Trimmer as advertised in The Gurnsley Echo.
I have always loved dogs and I have a dog myself which is a Shropshire Terrier. I talk to it a lot and it is very friendly with me although not always with other people so much.
I think I would enjoy the job and I know I would work hard. My CV is attached below.

Yours sincerely

Shirley Knott

Shirley Knott

Name:	Shirley Knott	
DOB:	22.03.1989	
Education:	St Bernard's Primary School	1993-2000
	Barkley High School	2000-2006
Qualifications:	GCSE maths, English, art, history, science.	
Present Occupation:	Part-time shop assistant	
Hobbies and Interests:	Animals, listening to music, dancing, swimming.	

▶ 1. Based on this letter, would Shirley be given an interview for the job? Give reasons for your answer.

....

....

▶ 2. Which of the four jobs did you choose to apply for?

....

▶ 3. On a separate piece of paper, write a letter of application for your chosen job. Include a short CV including your qualifications and experience. Think about any lessons you have learned from reading Shirley's letter.

▶ 4. Form four groups, each containing roughly the same number of people. Then:
- Collect all the letters of application from the members of the class and divide them into four sets – one for each job.
- Give one set of applications to each group.
- In your group, read and discuss the set of applications you have been given.
- Decide who would be most likely to get the job.
- Report your decision to the rest of the class and explain the reasons for your choice.

Interview 1

Watch video clip 1. Make notes while you are watching the video clip.

Jason is being interviewed for a job as a porter in a hotel. There are ten people being interviewed altogether and four jobs. Your task is to assess his chances. To do this you will need to work in a small group. Begin by discussing the questions below and writing down your answers. If you don't all agree – say so. You will probably need to watch the video clip several times and you might need to carry out some research to help you to answer the first two questions.

▶ 1. What does a hotel porter do?

▶ 2. What qualifications and personal qualities do you think you would need to become a hotel porter?

▶ 3. What was Jason wearing?

▶ 4. Do you think he was dressed correctly for an interview? Give reasons for your answer.

▶ 5. What was your first impression of Jason as he walked into the room?

▶ 6. What was it about him that gave these impressions?

▶ 7. What did Jason do – or not do – when Eleanor introduced herself to him? Say what impression he gave at this point.

▶ 8. What did Eleanor do to try to make Jason feel comfortable and relaxed?

Interview 1

▶ 9. Make a list of words or phrases which would describe Jason's behaviour and appearance at the very start of his interview.

▶ 10. Say why you have used these words to describe him.

▶ 11. How did Jason react when Eleanor began to read from his CV?

▶ 12. What made Jason nervous when Eleanor asked him how long he had worked in the restaurant?

▶ 13. How could you tell that he was nervous at this point?

▶ 14. Even though the interview has only just begun you will have already formed some opinions about Jason. At this stage, how would you rate his chances of getting the job? Based on what you have seen so far, give him a score between 1 and 10, where 1 means that he has absolutely no chance of getting the job and 10 means that he will almost certainly get the job. Ask each person in your group to give him a score and then work out the average.

▶ 15. In what ways, if any, do you think Jason will need to improve in the rest of the interview?

Interview 2

Watch video clip 2. Make notes while you are watching.

Tom is also being interviewed for a job as a porter in the hotel. Your job is to assess his chances. Again you will work in a small group. Begin by discussing the questions below and writing down your answers. If you don't all agree – say so. You will probably need to watch the video clip several times and you might need to carry out some research to help you to answer the first question.

▶ 1. What skills and qualities do you need when interviewing people?

▶ 2. What was Tom wearing?

▶ 3. Do you think he was dressed correctly for an interview? If not, say why not.

▶ 4. What were your first impressions of Tom as he walked into the room?

▶ 5. What was it about him that gave these impressions?

▶ 6. What did Tom do – or not do – when Eleanor introduced herself to him? Say what impressions he gave of himself at this point.

▶ 7. Eleanor said the same things to Tom as she said to Jason. Why do you think she did this?

▶ 8. Make a list of words or phrases which would describe Tom's behaviour and appearance at the very start of his interview.

▶ 9. Say why you have used these words to describe him.

Interview 2

▶ 10. When Eleanor began to read from Tom's CV, how did he react?

▶ 11. What impression do you think Tom's reaction gave?

▶ 12. Would you say that Tom was nervous? Give reasons for your answer.

▶ 13. What do you think Tom went on to say after, "Well, no because, to be honest..."

▶ 14. Even though the interview has only just begun you will have already formed some opinions about Tom. At this stage, how would you rate his chances of getting the job? Based on what you have seen so far, give him a score between 1 and 10, where 1 means that he has absolutely no chance of getting the job and 10 means that he will almost certainly get the job. Ask each person in your group to give him a score and then work out the average.

▶ 15. In what ways, if any, do you think Tom will need to improve in the rest of the interview?

Interview 3

Watch video clips 3a and 3b. Make notes while you are watching.

Jason's Interview (Video clip 3a)

▶ 1. What do you think Jason was describing to Eleanor at the beginning of the clip?

▶ 2. Do you think she would have been impressed with what he told her? Give reasons for your opinion.

▶ 3. Was it a good idea for Jason to admit that he was nervous? Again, give reasons for your answer.

▶ 4. In what ways did Eleanor try to relax Jason and put him at ease?

▶ 5. What do you think about Jason's reasons for leaving his present job?

▶ 6. Explain whether it was a good idea for Jason to admit that he had never worked in a hotel before?

▶ 7. What do you think he was going to say after, "I have thought about it and I think that..."?

▶ 8. In what ways, if any, has your opinion of Jason changed since the beginning of his interview?

Interview 3

Tom's Interview (Video clip 3b)

▶ 9. What kind of course do you think Tom was describing to Eleanor at the beginning of the clip?

▶ 10. Do you think she would have been impressed with his description of teamwork in his present job? Give reasons for your opinion.

▶ 11. What do you think about Tom's ability to work as part of a team?

▶ 12. Was it a good idea for Tom to say that he is good at being responsible? Again, give reasons for your answer.

▶ 13. What do you think Tom was going to say after, "I suppose it would be a bit strange at first but I think that..."?

▶ 14. In what ways, if any, has your opinion of Tom changed since the beginning of his interview?

Now it's decision time...

In your groups, discuss the two interviews and then answer these questions.

Would you give Jason the job?
Give reasons for your decision.

Interview 3

Would you give Tom the job?
Give reasons for your decision.

In a situation like this, how important are first impressions?
Were your first impressions correct or did you change your mind as you saw more of the two people?

Just the job?

Look at these jobs. They are all real jobs and were advertised in local and national newspapers.

1.

Assistant manager – pet store
Contract: Permanent
Hours: Not Specified
Salary: £14,940 – £15,500

2.

Sales consultant for jewellery retailer

This company is a well-established, high-end jewellery retailer offering an exclusive range of products through concessions within luxury department stores.
Your responsibilities will include:

- developing a client list
- driving sales
- communicating a knowledge of the brand
- maintaining high standards.

You will need these key attributes:

- a passion for luxury brands
- a smart professional appearance
- strong selling skills
- energy for contact with customers
- able to work within a team
- communication skills
- time management
- ability to learn new skills
- able to be flexible on evenings and weekends.

The successful candidate will have previous experience with a luxury brand and a commitment to delivering sensational service.

Part time. 3 days a week. £10 – £12 per hour. Bonus potential.

3.

Head of tourism for Cornwall

Tourism in Cornwall is a billion pound industry supporting over 40,000 jobs and contributing to over 24% of the county's economy.
You will be part of the executive team managing the delivery of Cornwall's Tourism Strategy.
Experience of public/private sector partnership working, sector capacity building, destination management and extensive knowledge of the visitor economy are vital to the success of this role.

4.

Teaching assistant

Hours: Not Specified
Working in a residential special school for pupils with complex special educational needs. The school has over 100 co-educational day and residential pupils on role, aged 5-19. The school has achieved outstanding OFSTED reports, holds Investors in People Status and is a National Support School.
Flexibility, humour and willingness to go the extra mile are essential for all our staff to ensure a high standard of support for all our pupils.
Salary: £12,371-£17,300. 48/52 weeks per annum, all school holidays.

5.

Head of business planning: British Antarctic Survey

The British Antarctic Survey focuses on some of the most important and challenging scientific problems in global scientific research. From its Cambridge headquarters it plans and delivers strategy, manages operations, employs 500 staff and runs three Antarctic research stations, two ships and a fleet of aircraft. We have a budget of over $50 million.
You will need to be dynamic and inspirational and work well in a team.
You must have an interest in polar science and experience of financial and risk management. An ability to travel in the Antarctic will be essential.
Salary £60,000 +

Just the job?

6.

Receptionist/administrative assistant
Contract: Permanent
Hours: Full Time
You will have NVQ Level 1 (or equivalent) together with reception/switchboard experience. You will have the ability to work both as part of a team and independently as well as the ability to prioritise your workload.
You must have RSA Level 1 typing and a working knowledge of Microsoft 2003 including Word and Excel.
Salary £13,027–£15,291 pa.

7.

Advertising telesales representative

Contract: Permanent

This is a new position working for a well-established publishing company.
You will have a proven track record within advertising telesales. The role will be office based Monday–Friday 9.00am – 5.00pm and you will contact local companies to sell advertising space. This will be split between cold calls and repeat business. You will be provided with the information on local businesses to cold call: sourced material from business directories, internet access, etc.
This is a great opportunity if you are target-driven, self-motivated and wish to work for a professional employer.

Basic Salary: £15,000
Opportunity to earn up to £25,000 with monthly bonuses.

8.

Supervisor: clothes store

Contract: Permanent
Hours: Not Specified
We are looking for great people to create, lead and drive great teams. We want our supervisors to lead from the front and think **BIG**. We believe that nothing is impossible!
You will want to continuously develop yourself and others and be willing to be held accountable in all that you do. You will be keen to have a 'right first time attitude' and believe in doing things well but simply.
To maintain our stores you will have a flair for working with our product - you will either come to us with that knowledge or we will work with you so that in time you know as much as we do about our merchandise.
You will have a desire to focus on our customers ensuring that they have the best possible shopping experience with us.
You will want to talk with our customers so that they feel welcome and valued in our stores.

Salary: £6.25 per hour

9.

Director of health and education: The Falkland Islands

You should have a substantial recent background in managing a people-friendly front line public service with the proven ability to work with senior professionals in fields such as health, social services and education.

3-year contract or possibly secondment.

10.

Assistant manager at major tourist attraction

Contract: Permanent
Hours: Not Specified
This will be the first of a series of attractions to be developed and this represents a unique opportunity for the right candidate to get in at the ground floor.
This is a position that calls for an excellent communicator, experienced in a customer-facing management position, ideally in the leisure sector.
They will be passionate about customer service and able to lead and motivate a team.
They should be financially able, computer literate and entrepreneurial in their approach as well as familiar with applicable UK employment and health and safety legislation.
The assistant manager will have responsibility for the day-to-day management of the site, managing staff and human resources as well as retail, ticketing, health and safety and security.
Most importantly, they will ensure the consistent delivery of a first-class visitor experience.

Salary: £18,000 per annum.

Just the job?

Read the job adverts on pages 20 and 21, then answer these questions.

Assistant manager pet store

▶ 1. What is meant by 'Hours: not specified'?

▶ 2. What would be your approximate weekly wage in this job?

▶ 3. Is this a fair wage for the job?

Yes, definitely ☐ Probably ☐ Possibly ☐ Definitely not ☐

▶ 4. How much responsibility would you have in this job?

A lot ☐ Some ☐ None ☐

▶ 5. Before you applied for this job, what extra information would you want?

Sales consultant for jewellery retailer

▶ 6. What is a bonus?

▶ 7. What is a retailer?

▶ 8. Could you do this job?

▶ 9. Which of the 'key attributes' do you have?

▶ 10. Which of the 'key attributes' don't you have?

▶ 11. If you work eight hours a day for three days a week in this job, what would you earn?

Just the job?

Head of tourism for Cornwall

▶ 12. What were your thoughts when you read this sentence?

'Experience of public/private sector partnership working, sector capacity building, destination management and extensive knowledge of the visitor economy are vital to the success of this role.'

That's obvious ☐ I don't quite understand this ☐ Eh??? ☐

▶ 13. What type of person would apply for this job? (Age, qualifications, interests, previous jobs, etc.)

▶ 14. What do you think would be the annual salary for this job?

£10K-£20K ☐ £30K-£40K ☐ £40K-£50K ☐ £60K-£70K ☐

(K stands for thousand)

▶ 15. Would you ever want to apply for a job like this? Give your reasons.

Teaching assistant

▶ 16. What qualifications are needed for this job?

▶ 17. What personal qualities are needed for this job?

▶ 18. What do you think your duties would be in this job?

▶ 19. This is a 'residential' school. How might this affect your working times?

Just the job?

▶ 20. Do you have what is needed to do this job? Give reasons for your answer.

▶ 21. If you started at the lowest salary, what would be your weekly wage?

£123 ☐ £173 ☐ £237 ☐ £332 ☐

Head of business planning: British Antarctic Survey

▶ 22. Where is this job based?

▶ 23. To get this job you would need 'the ability to travel in the Antarctic'. Where is the Antarctic?

▶ 24. What problems might there be in travelling and working in the Antarctic?

▶ 25. The salary for this job is £60,000 + per year. Roughly how much is this per week?

£6,150 ☐ £1,150 ☐ £650 ☐ £560 ☐

Receptionist/administrative assistant

▶ 26. What qualifications are needed for this job?

▶ 27. Do you have these qualifications?

▶ 28. If you wanted the job, would you have the ability and motivation to obtain these qualifications?

▶ 29. If you started at the highest salary, what would be your weekly wage?

£294 ☐ £152 ☐ £204 ☐ £348 ☐

Advertising telesales representative

▶ 30. What would you be doing in this job?

Just the job?

▶ 31. What are 'cold calls'?

▶ 32. Would you like this job? Give reasons for your answer.

▶ 33. If you received the basic salary without bonuses, what would be your weekly wage?

£158 ☐ £178 ☐ £228 ☐ £288 ☐

Supervisor: clothes store

▶ 34. From the job description, would you like this job?

Yes, definitely ☐ Probably ☐ Possibly ☐ Definitely not ☐

▶ 35. Give reasons for your answer to the previous question.

▶ 36. What would you earn for working a 40-hour week?

£150 ☐ £250 ☐ £350 ☐ £450 ☐

▶ 37. What qualifications do you need for this job?

Director of Health and Education: The Falkland Islands

▶ 38. Where are the Falkland Islands and how far away are they from Britain?

▶ 39. If you had a partner and young children, how might they be affected if you took this job?

▶ 40. What are the 'particular challenges of the Falkland Islands'?

▶ 41. What do you think the annual salary would be for this job?

£20,000 ☐ £60,000 ☐ £100,000 ☐ £250,000 ☐

Just the job?

Assistant Manager at Major Tourist Attraction

▶ 42. How much responsibility would you have in this job?

A lot ☐ Some ☐ None ☐

▶ 43. Which of the qualities/skills needed for this job do you think you have?

....

....

▶ 44. What is meant by 'this represents a unique opportunity for the right candidate to get in at the ground floor'?

....

....

▶ 45. What would be your weekly wage in this job?

£146 ☐ £246 ☐ £346 ☐ £446 ☐

▶ 46. Choose one of these jobs and write a letter of application. Use a separate piece of paper. Don't just choose the job which has the highest salary, choose a job that you would like to do and which you would have a good chance of getting.

Wages

Jay McGinty works in a shop. This is his payslip.

PAY ADVICE			**COSTCUTZ LTD**		
Date: 29 Febuary 2010			**Employee Number:** 213483		
Employee Name:	J. McGinly		**Tax Code:**	657L	
National Insurance Number:		PD198467C	**Deductions:**	Tax	£64.50
Payment:	40 hours @ £8.50	£320	**National Insurance:**		£32.10
			Net Pay:	**£225.40**	

Read through the payslip carefully and answer these questions.

▶ 1. According to the payslip, Jay earned £320. How much money did he actually receive?

....

▶ 2. On the payslip, what term is used to describe the amount of money Jay actually received?

....

▶ 3. What are deductions?

....

....

▶ 4. What is tax?

....

....

▶ 5. What is National Insurance?

....

....

▶ 6. What is a tax code?

....

....

Wages

▶ 7. There are four mistakes in the payslip. Find them and put a circle around each one. Next to the circle, write in a correction.

Work with a partner on this exercise.

▶ 8. One of you is going to play the part of Jay. The other person is Jay's boss. Flip a coin if you can't decide who should play which part. Act out this situation:

- Jay has worked out the mistakes in his/her pay.
- S/he wants to sort this out with the boss.
- The boss is a very strict person and hard to talk to.
- Jay plans what s/he is going to say.
- Jay approaches the boss. Jay is nervous. The boss is busy.
- What happens next?

▶ 9. What did you learn from this role-play? Working with your partner, make a list of things that would help someone starting work for the first time. Include hints on how to understand and check your payslip and also how to approach your boss. You might wish to present it in the form of a small advice leaflet.

A fair wage?

In 2008 the average wage in Britain was £479 per week. In the same year, a young man working in Manchester was paid around £120,000 per week.

While he was working in Manchester he was also paid money by companies other than his main employer:

- Nike paid him £6,000,000 per year
- Castrol paid him £2,000,000 per year.

In 2009 the young man moved to work in Madrid. Here are some figures about his new wages.

He was given a six-year contract with a pay rise each year. This is the breakdown of the pay structure:

- First year salary £9,500,000
- Second year £11,800,000
- Third year £14,800,000
- Fourth year £18,500,000
- Fifth year £23,100,000
- Sixth year £28,900,000

His new employers in Madrid paid his old employers in Manchester £80,000,000 so that they would agree to let him go.

Read the above information about wages and answer the following questions.

▶ **1. What was the young man's name?**

....

▶ **2. What was his job?**

....

▶ **3. If the average wage in Britain is around £480 per week, roughly how much is this per year?**

£2,500 ☐ £12,500 ☐ £25,000 ☐ £32,000 ☐

▶ **4. If you earned the average wage, how many years would it take you to earn what the young man earned in Manchester in one week?**

1 year ☐ Over 2 years ☐ Over 3 years ☐ Over 4 years ☐

▶ **5. Why did Nike and Castrol pay him money?**

....

....

▶ **6. What were his total earnings in one year when he worked in Manchester?**

£1.4m ☐ £4.2m ☐ £12.4m ☐ £14.2m ☐

A fair wage?

▶ 7. What is his weekly wage for his first year in Madrid?

£18,200 ☐ £28,200 ☐ £128,200 ☐ £182,000 ☐

▶ 8. What is his weekly wage for his sixth year in Madrid?

£55,000 ☐ £150,000 ☐ £255,000 ☐ £555,000 ☐

▶ 9. Write down his weekly wage for his sixth year in words.

....

▶ 10. In addition to paying his wages, the people in Madrid paid £80,000,000 to his employers in Manchester. How many people could be employed at the average wage for one year using this sum of money?

32 ☐ 320 ☐ 3,200 ☐ 32,000 ☐

▶ 11. Imagine that you are interviewing the young man as part of a radio programme about wages. Make a list of questions you would ask him.

....

....

....

....

....

....

....

▶ 12. Work with a partner. Swap questions and write down the answers you think the young man would give.

....

....

....

....

....

....

....

Talking

Listen to audio clip 1. Make notes while you are listening.

The four people in the audio clip are each doing an audition for the job of weather presenter on Radio Midway. This is a local station in your area with listeners of all ages and backgrounds. Your job is to decide who should get the job. Work in small groups. You can listen to the clips as many times as you wish.

▶ 1. Discuss the four possible presenters. Here are some questions that might help:

- Could they be clearly understood?
- Did their voice have the right sound or tone?
- Would the listeners like them?
- Did they sound as if they knew what they were talking about?
- Were they too loud, too quiet or just right?
- Did they create the right mood or atmosphere?

▶ 2. Fill in this report for the manager of Radio Midway. Give your opinion on each presenter and a score out of 10.

Name	***Opinions***	***Score***
Jack Frost		
April Showers		
Sean Summers		
Katie Winters		
The job should go to:		

▶ 3. Compare your opinions with those of the other groups. Based on the scores of all the groups, who would get the job?

Literacy levels at work

A recent survey carried out in Britain found that four out of ten employers have problems caused by poor standards of literacy and numeracy among their workers. In the retail sector, 69% of employers were worried about standards of reading and writing.

This survey was discussed on a local radio station. A number of people phoned in to express their opinions. Here is just one of those opinions:

> Young people today are nearly all illiterate. No wonder they can't do their jobs properly. And it's getting worse. In my day we didn't have computers and books but we could all read and write.
>
> Ernie Allbright aged 93¼

The ability to read and write is called 'literacy'. People who can't read and write are called 'illiterate'. Very few adults are illiterate; most have some level of reading and writing ability. They might have strengths and weaknesses in certain areas. The government has produced a 'framework for literacy' that sets out the levels.

Level	***Literacy (Reading) An adult at this level...***	***Equivalent to...***
Entry Level 1	*...understands short texts with repeated language patterns on familiar topics. ...can obtain information from common signs and symbols.*	*National Curriculum Level 1*
Entry Level 2	*...understands short straightforward texts on familiar topics. ...can obtain information from short documents, familiar sources and signs and symbols.*	*NC Level 2 (Level expected of a 7 year-old)*
Entry Level 3	*...understands short straightforward texts on familiar topics accurately and independently. ...can obtain information from everyday sources.*	*NC Level 3–4 (Level expected of an 11 year-old)*
Level 1	*...understands short straightforward texts of varying length on a variety of topics accurately and independently. ...can obtain information from different sources.*	*NC Level 5 (GCSE grades D–G)*
Level 2	*...understands a range of texts of varying complexity accurately and independently. ...can obtain information of varying length and detail from different sources.*	*NC Level 6–8 (GCSE grades A–C)*

Literacy levels at work

Ernie might be interested in figures from a recent survey. The aim of the survey was to find out about literacy levels among people of working age in **England**.

Level	*%*	*Number*
Entry level 1 or below	*3*	*1.1 million*
Entry level 2	*2*	*0.6 million*
Entry level 3	*11*	*3.5 million*
Level 1	*40*	*12.6 million*
Level 2 or above	*44*	*14.1 million*

These figures are for **Wales**:

Level	*%*	*Number*
Entry level 1 or below	*4*	*72,000*
Entry level 2	*3*	*54,000*
Entry level 3	*18*	*324,000*
Level 1	*37*	*680,000*
Level 2 or above	*38*	*700,000*

In **Northern Ireland**, 24% of adults came into the low skills category.

A survey in **Scotland** found that around 800,000 adults have very low levels of literacy. 23% were found to have low skills and a further 30% were found to have skills inadequate for the demands of the 'knowledge society' and the 'information age'.

Across **Europe** around 10% of the population is in the low skills category. In **Britain** around 20% of the population is in the low skills category. Eight million people are so poor at reading and writing that they cannot cope with the demands of modern life.

Since 2001 the number of adults in the workforce without level 2 has reduced from 7.1 million to 6.8 million.

In 2003 a survey found that 29% of adults (up to 11 million people) could not work out the area of a floor – either in square feet or in square metres. More than 10% could not understand the instructions on a packet of seeds. Less than a third of people managed to work out the amount of plastic covering needed to line a pond – even using a calculator, a pen and paper.

Read the information about levels of literacy and answer the questions.

▶ **1. What is 'literacy'?**

....

▶ **2. If someone is 'illiterate' what does this mean?**

....

Literacy levels at work

▶ 3. Are many people in Britain completely illiterate?

▶ 4. What is meant by 'working age'?

▶ 5. What percentage of the working population in **England** was in the low skills category?

▶ 6. Which four pieces of information about literacy are most worrying for the future of Britain?

▶ 7. Explain why they are so worrying.

▶ 8. Are there any signs of improvement? If so, what are they?

▶ 9. Imagine you are the presenter of the radio programme when Ernie phoned in. What would you say to him? Write your reply on a separate piece of paper.

▶ 10. Work with a partner or in a small group. Design a poster or flyer aimed at increasing the levels of literacy in people of your age group. Use some of the statistics and information to make people take notice.

Finally, be honest in answering these questions.

▶ 11. Would you be able to understand and follow the instructions on a packet of seeds?

Yes ☐ No ☐

▶ 12. What would you say is your literacy level?

Entry level 1 ☐ Entry level 2 ☐ Entry level 3 ☐ Level 1 ☐ Level 2 ☐

Magic

Watch video clip 4. Make notes while you are watching.

You are taking part in a training scheme to become a magician. There is good money to be made from magic these days but there is a lot of competition. Your course tutor is the international star, Jay Presto.

Welcome, apprentice magicians. I have prepared a test for you...

- Watch the video clip to see some magic tricks performed by a good friend of mine. When you have looked at them carefully, form small groups, discuss the tricks and work out how you think each one is done.
- Take turns to present your ideas to the rest of the class. You can criticise each other's ideas, but criticism must be constructive and supportive.
- Then, go back to your groups and re-think your ideas.
- Finally, discuss the tricks again with the whole class and decide on a 'most likely method' for each trick.

1. Sleight of hand card trick

2. Sponge balls trick

3. Six coin trick

Menu

Listen to audio clip 2. Make notes while you are listening.

You are training to be a chef. This is a test that has been set for you by Antonio Ciabatta, the head chef at The New York Grand Hotel.

The audio clip is a recipe for a simple, tasty and nutritious dish. Your job is to design and make a menu card based on the information in the audio clip. Here are some guidelines:

- You can listen to the audio clip as many times as you wish.
- List all the ingredients.
- List the equipment you will need (pans, dishes, etc.).
- Describe the method of preparing and cooking the dish.
- Write a first draft, go through it, and then make any changes that will improve it.
- Design the menu card, deciding on how it should be decorated.
- Put the final version of the recipe onto the menu card.
- Write the name of the dish at the top of the menu card.

Following instructions – know your napkins

You have just started working in a restaurant and the manager wants you to fold all the table napkins in a fancy way. This is how she wants them to look.

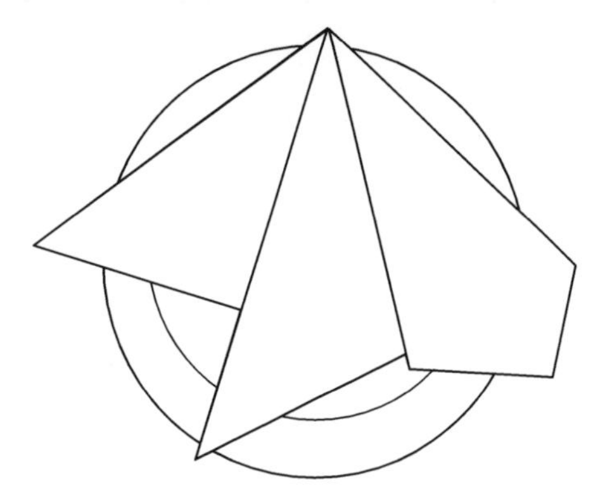

Listen to audio clip 3.

▶ 1. Work on your own and fold your napkin. You can play back the audio clip as many times as you wish.

▶ 2. Display your finished napkin.

▶ 3. Go round the room and look at all the napkins. What do you think of the general standard of napkin folding in the class?

....

▶ 4. How easy was it to follow the instructions? Give reasons for your opinions.

....

....

....

▶ 5. Do you think listening to instructions is the best way to learn something? Again, give reasons for your opinion.

....

....

....

▶ 6. What would have made the instructions easier to follow?

....

....

....

Following instructions – serviette style

Watch video clips 5a and 5b. The video clips show you how to make two different napkin folds.

▶ 1. On your own, practise making both napkin folds. You can watch the clips as many times as you wish.

▶ 2. Display your finished napkins.

▶ 3. Go round the room and look at all the napkins. What do you think of the general standard of napkin folding in the class?

....

▶ 4. How easy was it to follow the first set of instructions, which had no words? Give reasons for your opinions.

....

....

▶ 5. How easy was it to follow the second set of instructions, which did have words? Give reasons for your opinions.

....

....

▶ 6. Now form a small group and discuss the different ways of giving instructions. Draw up a list of guidelines for people who need to give instructions as part of their job.

....

....

....

....

....

....

....

....

....

....

....

....

Darts

Watch video clip 6a.

▶ 1. **You have just started work as a television sports commentator. Your first job will be reporting on a darts championship. This video is part of your training. Watch it carefully two or three times and then look at these guidelines.**

Speak clearly
Speak at a good speed. If you speak too fast you will not be understood. If you speak too slowly you will sound boring.
Vary the tone of your voice, making it higher or lower, louder or softer to suit the action.
Give some background information about the players.
Provide information about the scores. You will need to have some basic maths skills to do this.
Talk about the atmosphere in the room.
Refer to things the viewers might have missed or might not be aware of.
Don't talk too much. Make sure that what you say fits in with what is on the screen and don't try to describe too much of what people can see for themselves.
Point out things which could be exciting or interesting, especially when they are not obvious.
If you are working with someone else, take turns to speak but also talk to one another about what is going on.

▶ 2. **Add any other guidelines that you think might be helpful.**

Now watch video clip 6b. Make notes while you are watching. You can watch it as many times as you wish.

▶3. **Write a commentary to go with the video. You can watch it as many times as you wish.**

▶ 4. **Take turns to practise speaking your commentaries as the video is playing.**

▶ 5. **Which people in the class would make the best darts commentators? Give reasons for your choices.**

Introducing Z Factor

You work as a presenter on a local radio station. You have been given the job of interviewing 'Z Factor' – a new band. Here is some information about them and some questions that might help you to prepare for the interview.

The Official Z Factor Website HOME PAGE

Home | Gallery | Diary | Chat | Mobile | Shop | Sign up

Meet the band

Dawson Kendrick	Age 21	Guitar and vocals. Writes most of the band's songs with Angelica. Influenced by Oasis and Radiohead. Likes to paint.
Angelica Hough	Age 20	Keyboards and vocals. Writes most of the band's songs with Dawson. Influenced by Gabrielle and Annie Lennox. Loves poetry.
Hovis Bean	Age 23	Percussion. Influenced by Jarvis Cocker. Into green issues.
Jessica Sorensen	Age 21	Woodwind. Influenced by Nestor Torres. Runs an animal sanctuary.

History

Formed in 2009 when Dawson and Angelica met Hovis and Jessica at Glastonbury. They were in different bands at the time. First album, 'Recovery Position' sold 500,000 copies in three weeks and is expected to go platinum.

Music

'Z Factor' are not your run-of-the-mill guitar band. They experiment with rhythms and their albums contain dance tracks as well as reflective, slower compositions. The lyrics to their songs are thoughtful but optimistic.

Current Tour Dates

Belfast	March 15	SOLD OUT
Dublin	March 17	SOLD OUT
Glasgow	March 19	
Newcastle	March 21	
Liverpool	March 23	SOLD OUT
Sheffield	March 24	SOLD OUT
Birmingham	March 26	
Bristol	March 28	
London	March 30	SOLD OUT

Latest Album

'Festival for Freaks'
Release date: March 1
Contains the hit single 'Knot Alone' and 14 more tracks.

Knot Alone
You tie me up with riddles and I can't break free
I try to understand what I can't see
And now you leave me here all on my own
You pull me tighter like a knot alone.

For every album sold, 10p will be donated to the charity 'Life Changes'.

Introducing Z Factor

Read the 'Z Factor' web page and answer these questions.

▶ 1. **How many people are in the band?**

▶ 2. **Who is the youngest member of the band?**

▶ 3. **Who is the oldest member of the band?**

▶ 4. **Who are the songwriters in the band?**

▶ 5. **Which member of the band do you think has a made-up name?**

▶ 6. **What are percussion instruments? Give two examples.**

▶ 7. **From what you have read about Jessica, what instruments do you think she plays?**

Guitar ☐ Trumpet ☐ Flute ☐ Saxophone ☐ Piano ☐ Clarinet ☐

▶ 8. **What is the title of the latest single from Z Factor?**

Festival for Freaks ☐ Knot Alone ☐ Life Changes ☐

▶ 9. **If the new album sells 500,000 copies how much will be raised for charity?**

£5,000,000 ☐ £500,000 ☐ £55,000 ☐ £50,000 ☐ £5,000 ☐ £500 ☐

▶ 10. **How popular are Z Factor? Give reasons for your opinions.**

▶ 11. **What type of people would be fans of Z Factor? Give reasons for your answer.**

Introducing Z Factor

▶ 12. Now write down some questions you would like to ask each member of the band.

Dawson	
Angelica	
Hovis	
Jessica	

Finish the lyrics

The band 'Z Factor' has a contract to produce a new album. Unfortunately, the two members of the band who write the songs, Angelica and Dawson, fell off stage at the Blastonbury Festival and are in hospital. They have left these unfinished lyrics.

▶ 1.

You're not the one for me
It's obvious
Although you just can't see
It's obvious
Your life is not like mine
It's obvious
End of the line...

▶ 2.

Can you lend me your heart -
for a night?
Until I can be sure I'm all right

Can you lend me your heart when
I cry?
If you know it will help me get by

Chorus:
It's only your heart that I'm after -
not all of you
It's only...

▶ 3.

At first I thought you were special
Now I know you're really a fool
You're so immature and pathetic
You should be still in school

I was going to send you a letter
To tell you that we're through
But I thought it would be better
To say it on the phone to you

Chorus:
Delete my number and forget me
Don't email and don't...

▶ 4.

The trees are slowly dying
But the sun shines on
It will still be shining
When the world has gone

The rivers are still flowing
Into rising seas
And the ashes are blowing
In the...

The record company has asked you to finish the lyrics to the four songs. You have been given these guidelines:

- **Find a partner – someone you can work with and who is on the same wavelength as you.**
- **Read the lyrics and discuss what you think the song is about. Is it a story? Does it have a message?**
- **Choose one song to start with and copy it onto a piece of paper.**
- **Discuss ways in which the lyrics to that song could continue.**
- **Write the next two or three lines.**
- **Read them out loud and see if they work.**
- **Change them if you think they can be improved.**
- **Carry on and finish the song.**
- **Read the whole song aloud and discuss it.**
- **Make any improvements you think are needed.**
- **Write out all the lyrics neatly on another piece of paper.**
- **Give the song a title.**
- **Move on to the next song and repeat the process.**

Breaking news

Read these emails which have just arrived at a national radio station from reporters around the world.

To: News Desk

From: Josh Khan

Subject: Financial Conference, Madrid, Monday

World leaders agree on new plans to help developing countries.

- £36 billion to be made available for renewable energy projects over next ten years.
- £5 billion in debts to US, Japan and EU to be written off.
- Health care projects to be funded in Africa. Cost £14 billion per year for three years.
- Agreement not to import cheap goods made by workers in poor conditions or working for less than $10 per day.

Original plans opposed by France and Italy. Changes made overnight and agreement reached early this morning.
Prime Minister to make statement later today.

To: News Desk

From: Primula Maybank

Subject: Dean de Deville dead

93-year-old film actor injured yesterday diving into river on a rafting holiday. Taken to hospital in LA. Died at 01.35 this morning. Thousands of floral tributes from fans.
Played the lead in 'Lassie'. Starred in many action movies including: 'Die Like a Hamster' and 'Hamster v Gerbil'.
Never won an Oscar. Nominated four times.
From the age of 14 worked in circus as a human cannonball. He got fired.
Took acting lessons and worked as a part-time brain surgeon until discovered by studio boss, Irving Heinkel.
Dean's wife, Dolores, and their Doberman dog, Duke, expected to attend funeral next Thursday.

Breaking news

To: News Desk

From: Claire Doyle

Subject: General Election results

Two hours after polling stations closed.
First ten results show huge swing to Lib Dems.
Labour share of vote down by over 20%.
Conservatives up by 8%.
Lib Dems up by over 12%.
Prime Minister scrapes home by 984 votes.
Josie Jones: "This looks like being a disaster for us but we can blame nobody but ourselves."
Daniel Caramel: "It's too soon to predict anything."
Brian Clogg: "It's time for a change."

To: News Desk

From: Erskine Waldebloom

Subject: Floods in Finland

Early spring thaw has caused rivers to burst their banks. Elks swept away and found in trees hundreds of miles away.
School cancelled in Kokkola as caretaker's canoe sinks. Children celebrate and fall in river. Rescued by fishermen.
"It was cold," says Roni Rikonen (13).
Prime Minister promised to fly out and help. Sand bags and dry socks needed.
Fin Flood Fund appeal set up.

Your job is to prepare a short news programme for the radio station. Here are your guidelines:

- **Form a small group of no more than five people.**
- **Choose one person to be the director.**
- **Write a script using the information in the emails from the reporters.**
- **The length of the programme should be two minutes.**
- **Divide up the script between different people.**
- **Practise reading the news and get the timing right.**
- **Be prepared for any items of 'breaking news'.**
- **Be ready to go 'on air' when you are given the signal.**

Breaking news

Breaking News: Football manager agrees with ref!

Semi-final of World Cup. Germany lose 1 – 0 to Italy. Penalty in final minute of extra time. German manager, Heinz Bienz, said: "I didn't really see what happened but the ref is a fair man and I am happy to agree with him."
German captain, Berndt Ost, said: "I tackled Carlo Confetti and the ref said it was a foul. I apologised of course and they scored from the penalty."

Breaking News: Hedgehog Flu

Scientists fear an epidemic of hedgehog flu. Three hedgehogs in Surrey found sneezing in a park three days ago. One has since died. Reports that it was squashed by a milk float denied by health minister, Barbara Biddicomb: "This is serious. If you see a sneezing hedgehog, don't go near it. That's the point. You must report it."
Laboratories are making serum. It can be cured if caught early. Symptoms include coughing and falling asleep curled up in a ball.

Breaking News: Comet heading for earth

Only 26,000,000 miles away. Spotted on 1 April by Prof. B. Rainey. On course to crash into retail park in St Helens. Prime Minister says: "Don't panic. It might miss us and hit Pluto." Disney studios not happy.

Breaking News: Granny wins 'Britain's Got X-Factor'

98-year-old Ethel Moss wins talent competition. Sings 'Mamma Mia' on a bike and juggles goldfish. Signs contract to star in Las Vegas. Record set to top charts. Husband, Alf, says: "Her mother was over the moon when she won."

News headlines

Listen to audio clip 4. Make notes while you are listening.

There are four telephone calls in the audio clip. Each has been made by a reporter to the news desk of your local radio station. Your job is to produce the news headlines based on the four stories from the reporters. Here are your guidelines:

- Work in small groups.
- Base the headlines on what the reporters have said but put the information into your own words.
- You can listen to the audio clips as many times as you wish.
- The headlines must fit into a 30-second time slot.
- Decide on who does what. Everyone can help to write the script but you will need a director, an announcer and a newsreader.
- You have thirty minutes before you go live on air.
- In that time you will need to rehearse at least once.
- Speak clearly.

Picture this

For many jobs you need to be observant. For example: a security guard, an air-traffic controller, a referee, a nurse or doctor... and of course a spy! Could you do any of these jobs? Are you observant? Try some simple tests to find out.

You have one minute to look at this picture. *Do not* ***take notes or copy any part of the drawing.***

Picture 1

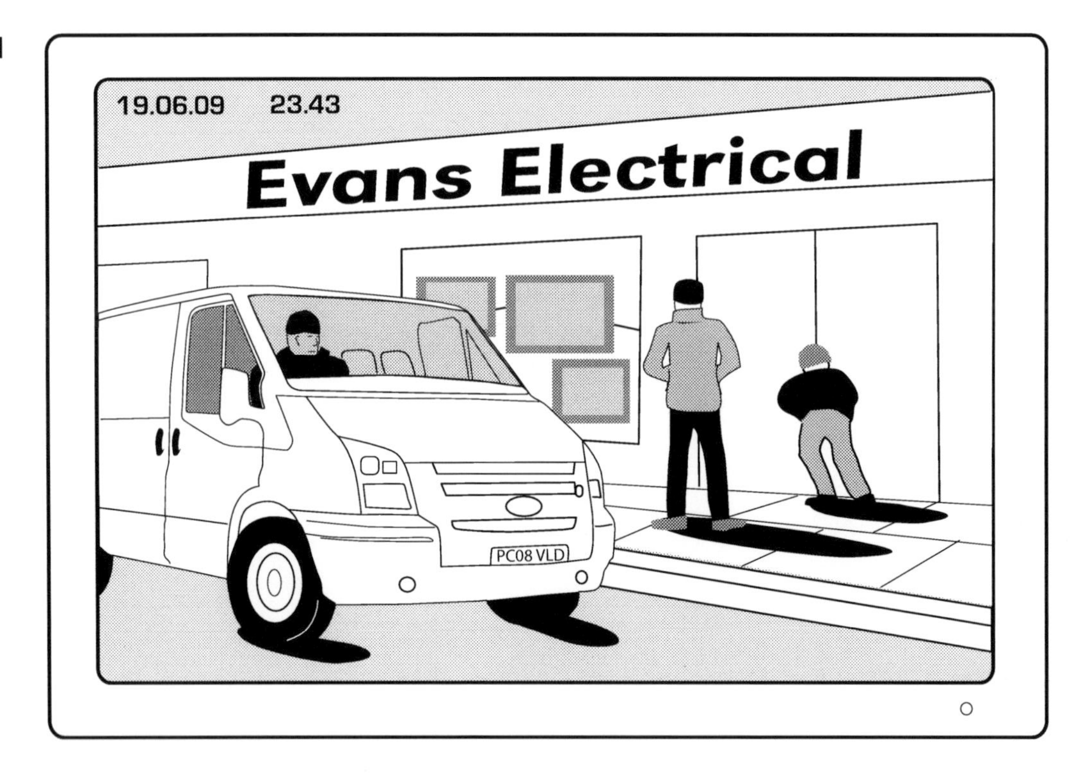

You have one minute to look at this picture. *Do not* ***take notes or copy any part of the drawing.***

Picture 2

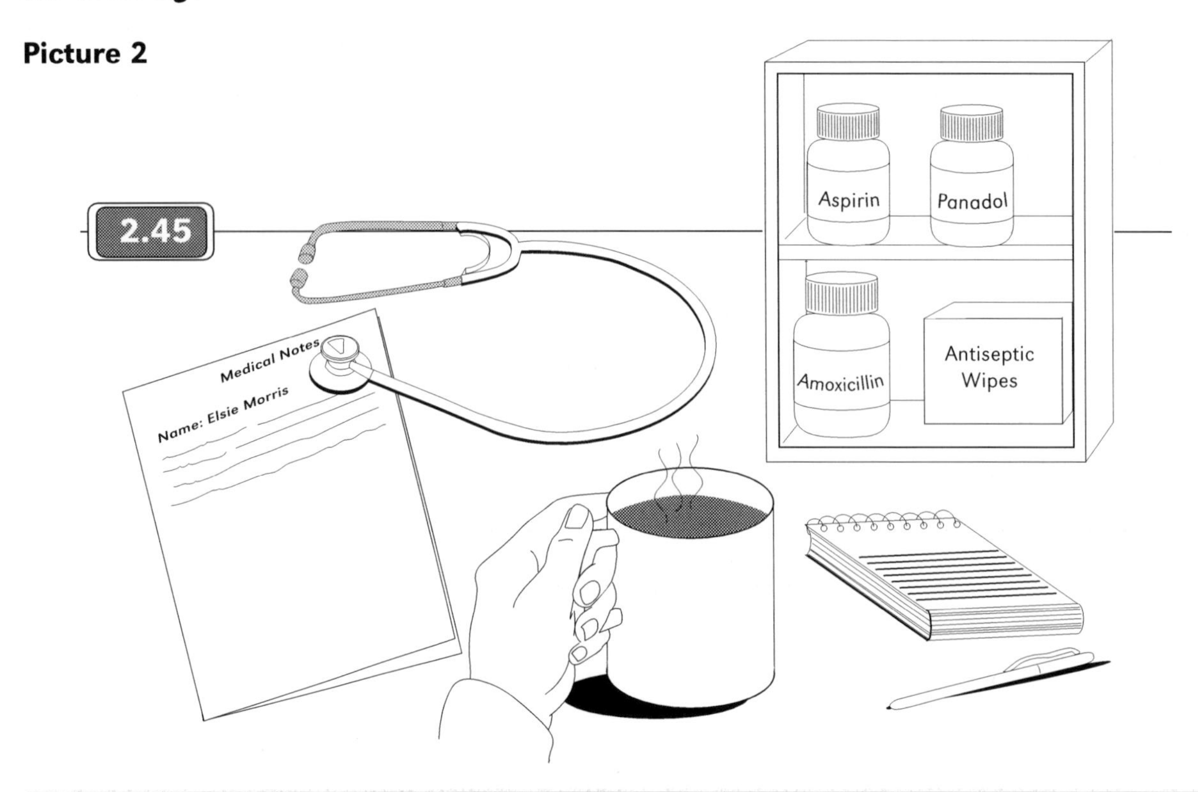

Picture this

▶ 1. How many people are in Picture 1? Describe them.

....

....

....

▶ 2. What is the location in Picture 1?

....

▶ 3. What is happening in Picture 1?

....

....

▶ 4. On a separate piece of paper, draw Picture 1 from memory. If you are not a good artist, just draw a rough sketch but include as many details as you can remember and make it as accurate as you can.

▶ 5. How many people are in Picture 2?

....

▶ 6. What is the location in Picture 2?

....

▶ 7. What objects are shown in Picture 2?

....

....

▶ 8. On a separate piece of paper, draw Picture 2 from memory.

▶ 9. How easy did you find it to remember what you saw in the pictures? Tick as many boxes as you wish.

I found it very easy with both pictures.	
I found it really difficult with both pictures.	
I found it quite hard with both pictures.	
I found it quite easy with both pictures.	
I found it easier with the second picture.	

Picture that

▶ 1. You and your partner have each been given a different picture to look at. Do not let your partner see your picture. You have one minute to look at the picture. **Do not** take notes or copy any part of the drawing.

Picture 1

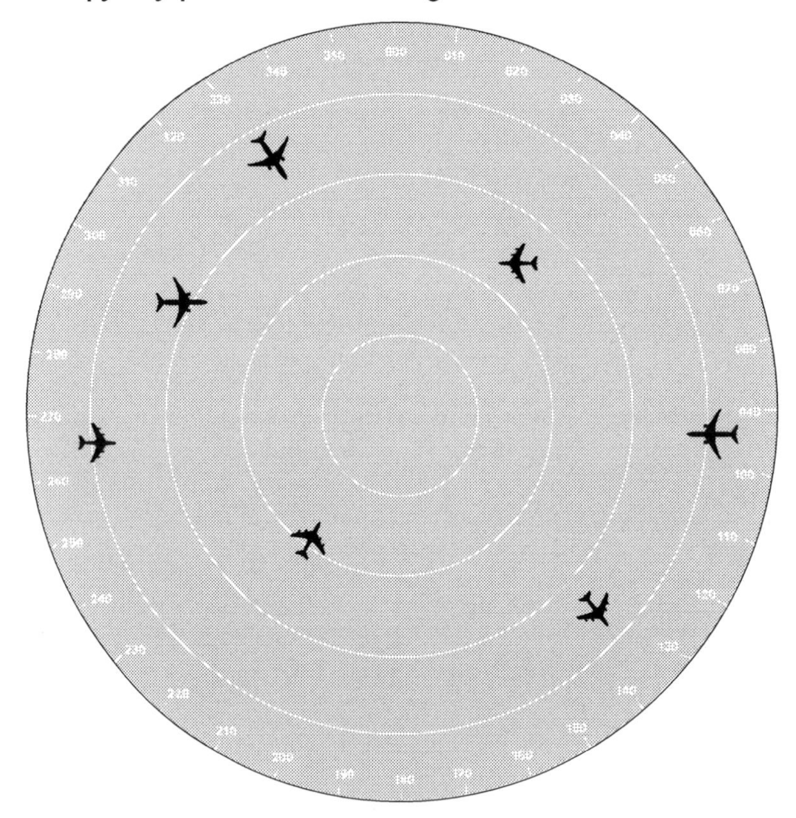

▶ 1. The person who saw Picture 1 should begin.

Tell your partner what was in the picture. Their job is to draw the picture from your instructions. They should use a separate piece of paper. You are not allowed to draw any of it for them. Make sure you describe it clearly.

▶ 2. Once you have both drawn your pictures, compare the pictures you have drawn with the original pictures. Discuss how well you both described the pictures and how well you both copied the descriptions. Then tick as many of the boxes below as you wish.

The picture I drew was very like the original.	
The picture I drew was quite like the original.	
The picture I drew was nothing like the original.	
My partner gave a very clear description of the picture.	
My partner gave quite a clear description of the picture.	
My partner gave a poor description of the picture.	
The picture my partner drew was very like the original.	
The picture my partner drew was quite like the original.	
The picture my partner drew was nothing like the original.	
I gave a very clear description of the picture.	
I gave quite a clear description of the picture.	
I gave a poor description of the picture.	

Picture that

▶ 2. **You and your partner have each been given a different picture to look at. Do not let your partner see your picture. You have one minute to look at the picture. Do not take notes or copy any part of the drawing.**

Picture 2

▶ 2. **The person who saw Picture 2 should go next.**

Tell your partner what was in the picture. Their job is to draw the picture from your instructions. They should use a separate piece of paper. You are not allowed to draw any of it for them. Make sure you describe it clearly.

▶ 3. **Once you have both drawn your pictures, compare the pictures you have drawn with the original pictures. Discuss how well you both described the pictures and how well you both copied the descriptions. Then tick as many of the boxes below as you wish.**

The picture I drew was very like the original.	
The picture I drew was quite like the original.	
The picture I drew was nothing like the original.	
My partner gave a very clear description of the picture.	
My partner gave quite a clear description of the picture.	
My partner gave a poor description of the picture.	
The picture my partner drew was very like the original.	
The picture my partner drew was quite like the original.	
The picture my partner drew was nothing like the original.	
I gave a very clear description of the picture.	
I gave quite a clear description of the picture.	
I gave a poor description of the picture.	

Picture these

▶ 1. You are a student nurse and you have been given this diagram as part of your training. You have one minute to look at the diagram. **Do not** take notes or copy any part of the drawing.

Diagram 1

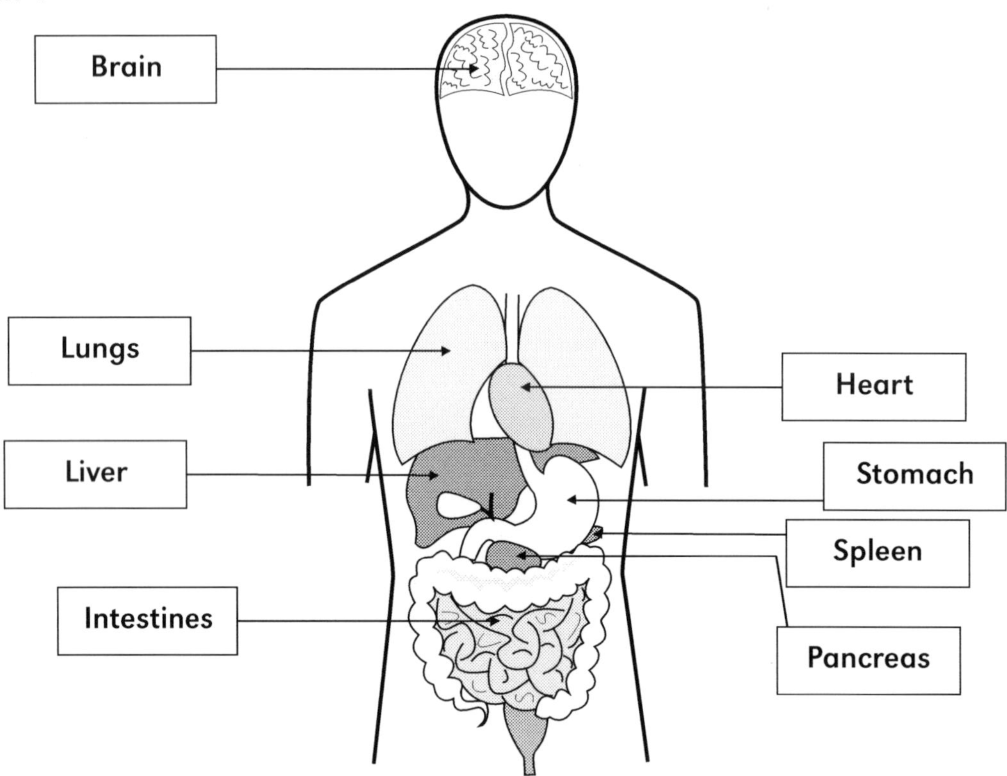

▶ 2. You work in an electrical store. You need to learn about the products you sell. You have one minute to look at this diagram. **Do not** take notes or copy any part of the drawing.

Diagram 2

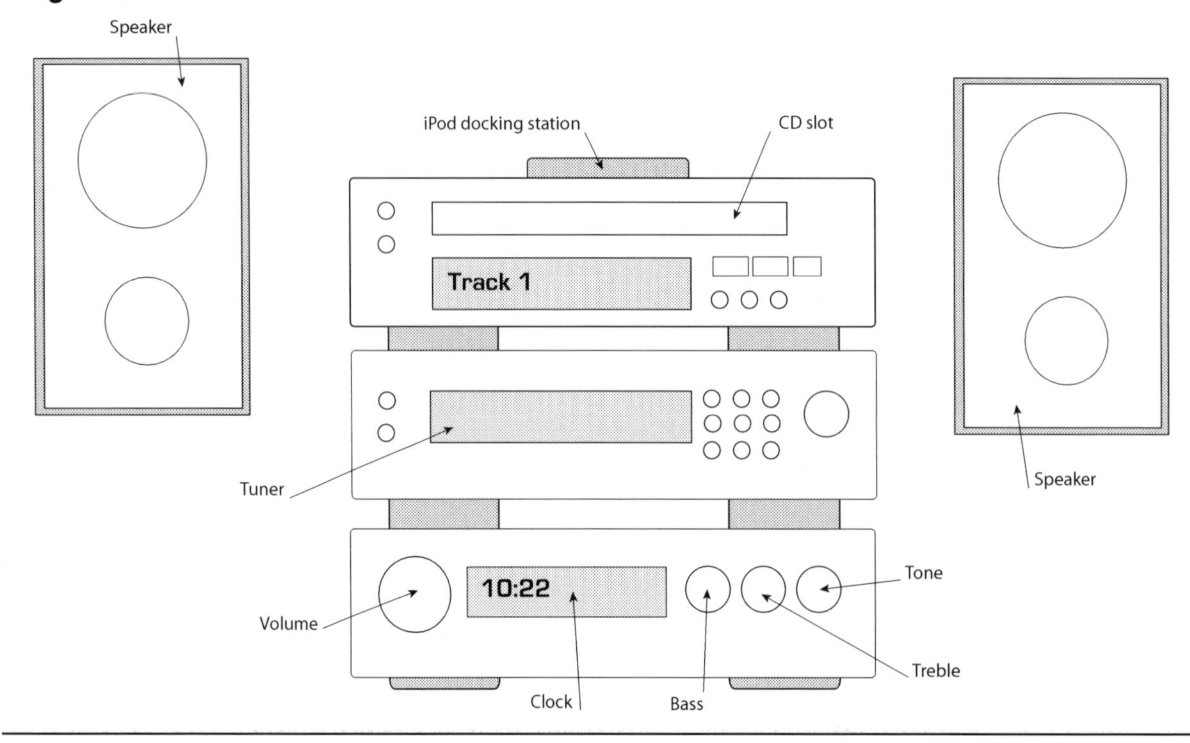

Picture these

▶ 3. **This is diagram 1 with the labels missing. Use your memory to help you write them in the boxes.**

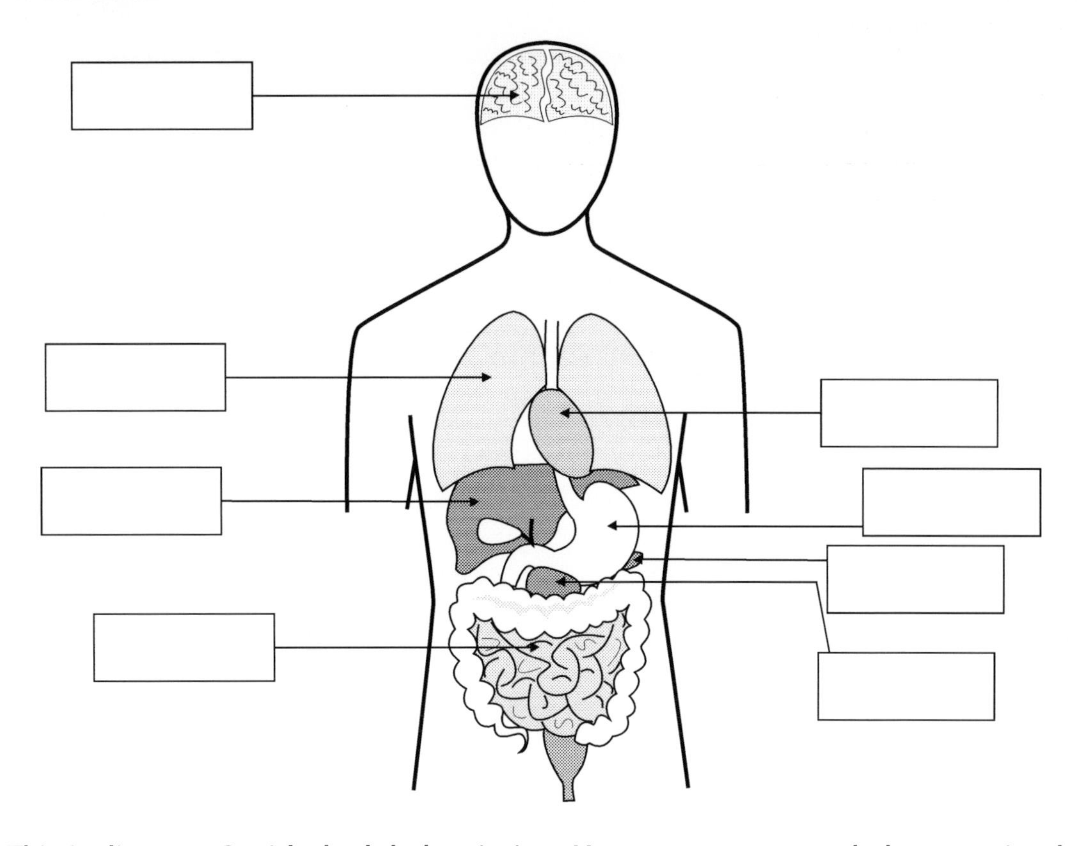

▶ 4. **This is diagram 2 with the labels missing. Use your memory to help you write them in the boxes.**

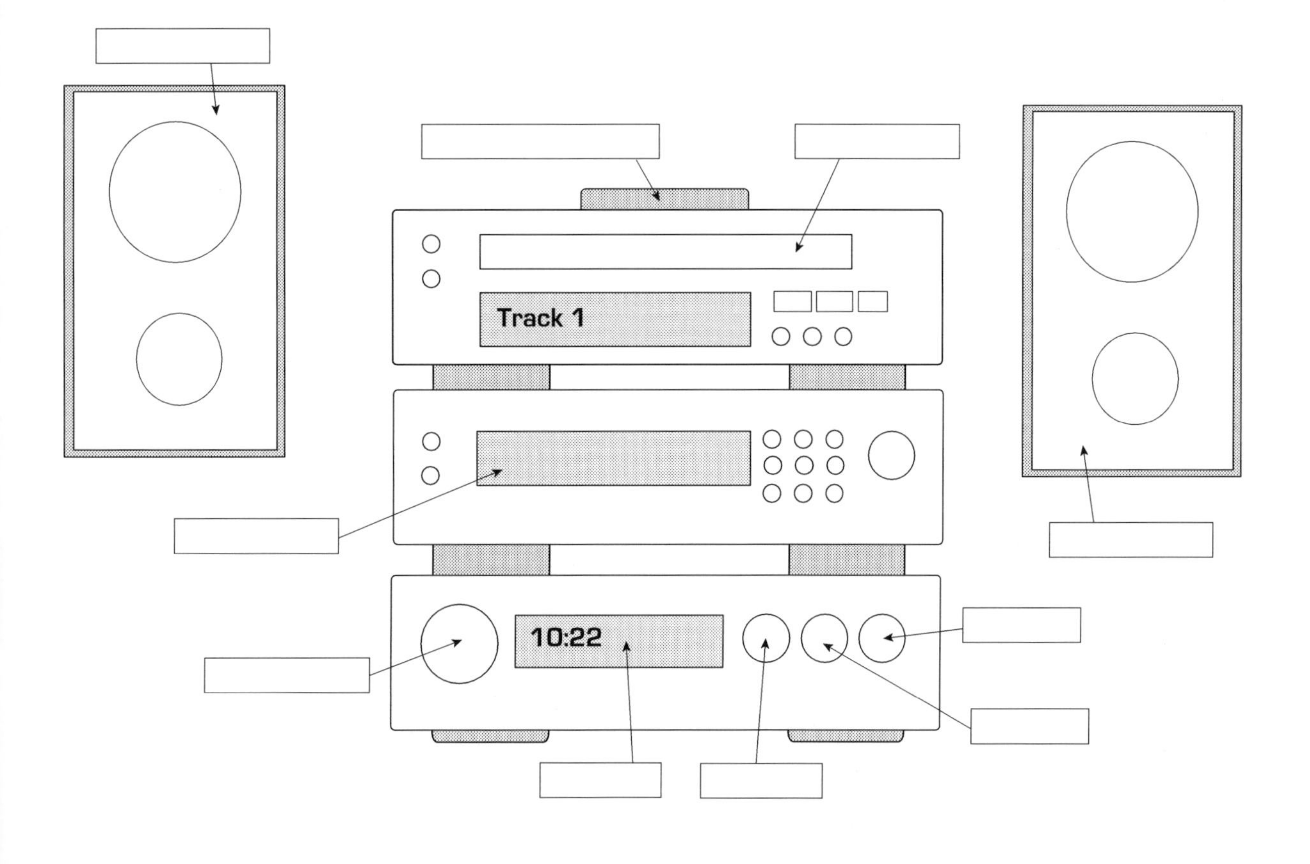

Picture these

▶ 5. In many jobs you have to draw diagrams to describe things to customers and colleagues. Could you do it? Let's find out.

Take a piece of paper and draw a labelled diagram of something you know well. Here are some guidelines.

- Choose a common object (television, computer, car, bike, iPod, radio, toaster, microwave oven).
- Keep the diagram simple.
- Draw clearly and don't include too much unnecessary detail.
- Remember it is a diagram, not a picture.
- Make sure that the diagram is the right size. Use as much of the page as you need but leave space for the labels.
- Show all the main parts of the object.
- Label the diagram neatly.
- Draw straight lines from the parts to the labels.
- Put the labels outside the drawing.

The Daily Blag

Jody Maloney is a reporter on The Daily Blag. She was typing these reports when her computer was hit by a virus. It deleted some of the words. They are in boxes beneath the articles. Put them back in the correct places.

Dog Saves Hamster's Life

Rupert the Rotweiler didn't _______ when his little _______, Harry the _______, fell into the fish _______. Rupert ran to his _______, seven-year-old Dylan Donlan, and raised the _______.
"He barked and barked," said Dylan, "and then he ________ my arm in his mouth and pulled me into the _______."
By the time Dylan's dad, Dennis, arrived to ______, Harry was back on ______land.

"He couldn't get out of the pond and a ______ fish was after him. Rupert ________off the fish and I pulled Harry out," said Dylan.
Dennis has _______ in the pond at his home in Halifax, and ________Rupert for the annual 'Pet Hero' award. Harry seems to have ______ no lasting damage and yesterday he was playing _________ in the garden with Rupert and Dylan.

entered	alarm	suffered	big	scared	pal
help	Hamster	happily	garden	dry	pond
owner	grabbed	filled	panic		

Interest Rates Set to Rise

The Bank of _______ is expected to ______ interest rates to ______ tomorrow. Financial experts predict that the current ________ climate has made an increase inevitable. This will affect ________ and increase the burden on house-buyers. ________ providers are expected to increase their rates by at least 0.5%. The Prime Minister made a _________ in Parliament.

inflation	economic	statement	England
increase	4.5%	Mortgage	

The Daily Blag

You now have a more difficult job.

You must write newspaper articles based on the headlines below, including the words and numbers in the boxes. Use separate pieces of paper for each article. Here are some guidelines:

- Think about what happened.
- Include the names of people in the article and say something about them.
- Include quotes from people involved.
- Make the opening sentence short and interesting.
- Make the article easy to read.
- Keep it simple and clear but don't insult your readers by making it too simple.
- Check your spelling and punctuation.
- Give the article a good ending.

The Fastest Woman in the World!

Olympic Games	Final	Susan Strider	Manchester
10.46	21 years of age	Parents, Mike and Angie	Gold Medal
London	2012		

Family Survives Blast

Gas explosion	Bungalow	Sleeping	Fire
Mum, Dad and three children	Neighbours	Digging in the rubble	
Emergency services	Midnight	Budgie	

It's a Landslide!

General Election	Conservative	Labour	Liberal Democrats
Prime Minister	Majority	Seats	Parliament
Government	Defeated	Votes	

Pedalo power

Listen to audio clip 5. Make notes while you are watching.

Work on your own to answer these questions about the story on the news.

▶ 1. Complete this fact-file about Brian. Include any facts that are mentioned in the story.

BRIAN CHUFF: Facts

▶ 2. Now write down your opinions about Brian. For example, you can say whether you think he was brave or sensible and whether he is a good role model to his children.

BRIAN CHUFF: Opinions

▶ 3. Why was Brian offered money by *The Daily World*?

....

....

Pedalo power

▶ 4. You are a reporter for *The Daily World*. Complete this story. Use a separate sheet of paper if you need one.

PEDALO POWER: BRITISH MAN SETS OFF ROUND THE WORLD

The Daily World is proud to announce that we are helping 32-year-old Brian Chuff to become the first man to sail round the world in a pedalo. Yesterday, he

Now form a small group to work on the next part of this exercise.

The manager of The Slug and Cabbage is putting on a 'Welcome Back Chuffy' party. There will be a press conference afterwards.

▶ 5. On a separate piece of paper, make a list of between five and ten interesting questions which reporters might ask Brian and his wife. Leave gaps for answers.

▶ 6. Think about the answers that Brian and his wife might give to these questions. Write them down in the gaps.

▶ 7. Using your questions and answers, act out the press conference.

The fishing line

Listen to audio clip 6. Make notes while you are listening.

Answer these questions on your own.

▶ 1. What were the names of:

a) the radio station? ....

b) the presenter? ....

c) the programme? ....

▶ 2. What was each of these people doing?

a) Eric Hopley ....

b) Amy Johnson ....

c) Frank Bodger ....

d) Hugh Williams ....

▶ 3. The presenter said that it would be 'a thrilling three days'. Would you agree with this? Give reasons for your answer.

....

....

....

Now work in small groups to discuss and answer these questions. Imagine that you work for a local radio station.

▶ 4. The radio station manager is a keen fisherman and wants to include more fishing programmes. You don't think that fishing is a good choice of sport to include in a radio programme. Draft an email to him with your opinions.

▶ 5. The station manager has sent you to cover the second day of the fishing championships. He wants you to interview one of the people mentioned in the first programme. Choose one of them and on a separate piece of paper write a list of interesting questions to ask them.

▶ 6. Think about the answers you might get to your questions. Then act out the interview.

Public speaking

Watch video clips 7a-c. Answer these questions on your own.

Video clip 7a.

▶ 1. Who was making the speech?

▶ 2. What was the purpose of the speech?

▶ 3. How good was the speech? Give it a mark out of 10.

▶ 4. Give reasons for your opinion.

▶ 5. Imagine that you are Sarah. Describe your feelings after listening to the speech.

Video clip 7b.

▶ 6. Who was making the speech?

▶ 7. What was the purpose of the speech?

▶ 8. How good was the speech? Give it a mark out of 10.

▶ 9. Give reasons for your opinion.

▶ 10. Imagine that you are Nana. Describe your feelings after listening to the speech.

Public speaking

Video clip 7c.

▶ 11. Who was making the speech?

▶ 12. What was the purpose of the speech?

▶ 13. How good was the speech? Give it a mark out of 10.

▶ 14. Give reasons for your opinion.

▶ 15. Imagine that you are Mr Roscoe. Describe your feelings after listening to the speech.

Now carry out these activities as a class.

▶ 16. Compare your opinions and scores for the three speeches. Did you all agree about which speech was worst and which was best?

▶ 17. Take each speech in turn and discuss the ways in which it could be improved.

▶ 18. Draw up a list of things you should NOT do when making a speech.

Speaking in public

You might be surprised at how many times you have to speak in front of other people. Most people don't find it easy...

Fatima

It was my first day in my new job and I was really nervous. I was just sitting down and the boss said, "Okay everybody, we've got someone new in the office today."

I was hoping she didn't mean me but then she said, "Her name is Fatima and she's over there looking very nervous, but I'm going to ask her to introduce herself and tell us all a little bit about herself."

I could feel myself going red and my mind went blank. I sort of waved my hand for some stupid reason and said, "Hello, I'm Fatima and I've just started today. I'm from..."

Tom

The lecturer was really nice and told us all about the course. He said we were going to learn how to improve our communication skills. Then he said, "We're going to start with a simple role-play."

I felt sick. I've always hated doing role-plays. I should have got a note from my Mum saying 'I'm excused from role-plays for medical reasons.'

I told myself that he probably wouldn't pick on me first but then he said, "Tom, you are the pilot of a plane. You are running out of fuel and have to make an emergency landing. What do you say to the passengers?"

I was speechless. I just sat there for ages and then I said, "Hello, this is the captain speaking..."

Sarah

I'd been working in the cake shop for a week. The manager said, "I'm going out for an hour, Sarah. You're in charge until I get back."

I was terrified but it was fairly quiet at first. Then, four people came in together and asked me if we made wedding cakes. I told them that we did and one of them said, "Can you give us some idea of the different kinds of cakes you make and how much they cost?"

It was like a bad dream. I'm still embarrassed now when I think about it. I said, "Yes, well we do all different kinds of wedding cakes but..."

Speaking in public

Patrick

I was doing work experience at a big hotel and I was helping on the reception desk. A group of six people were checking in. They were Americans. One of them turned to me, looked at my badge and said, "Hi Patrick. We're only staying for three days. Can you tell us some of the places we should visit while we're here?"

"I'm sorry," I said, "I'm only on work experience."

"Yes, but you do live here don't you?" said the man.

"Yes," I said.

"Okay, so tell us the best places to see."

I took a deep breath. "Well," I said, "maybe you could..."

Read the stories of Fatima, Tom, Sarah and Patrick. Think about each situation in turn and answer these questions.

Fatima

▶ 1. **Was this a good thing for Fatima's boss to do? Give reasons for your answer.**

▶ 2. **How was Fatima affected by what her boss said?**

▶ 3. **If you were in a similar position and your boss asked you to introduce yourself, what would you say?**

Tom

▶ 4. **What is a role-play?**

Speaking in public

▶ 5. Why do you think Tom hated role-plays?

▶ 6. Was it fair of the lecturer to start off the course in this way? Give reasons for your answer.

▶ 7. Write out your version of what the pilot of the plane would say.

Sarah

▶ 8. Why was Sarah terrified when the manager left her in charge?

▶ 9. Do you think it helped Sarah in any way to be left in charge like this? Give reasons for your answer.

▶ 10. What would you have said to the people who asked about the wedding cakes?

Speaking in public

Patrick

▶ 11. Why did Patrick say, "I'm only on work experience"?

▶ 12. Was this a good thing to say? Give reasons for your answer.

▶ 13. If an American tourist asked you about places to visit in your area, what would you say?

Now work with a partner or in a small group.

▶ 14. Take turns to read out your answers to questions 3, 7, 10 and 13.

▶ 15. Discuss what each person said and how well they said it.

▶ 16. On a separate piece of paper, write out a list of guidelines to help young people to cope in situations like these.

Listen carefully

Listen to audio clip 7a.

▶ 1. Follow the instructions in the audio clip.

As a class, discuss and answer these questions.

▶ 2. How easy was it to remember the instructions?

....

▶ 3. What would have made it easier to concentrate and remember the instructions better?

....

▶ 4. What distracted you or stopped you from concentrating?

....

▶ 5. Why were you not allowed to make notes?

....

▶ 6. On a separate piece of paper, draw up a list of guidelines for spies who have to follow secret instructions that they can only listen to once.

Now listen to audio clip 7b.

▶ 7. Follow the instructions in the audio clip.

As a class, discuss and answer these questions.

▶ 8. Were your guidelines helpful and was it easier to follow the instructions this time?

....

▶ 9. Make any changes you think might improve your guidelines.

▶ 10. You will probably never actually be a spy, so how can this exercise be useful to you in work situations? Give some examples. Clue – think about situations in which you might be given verbal instructions.

....

....

....

....

Customer care 1

Watch video clip 8. Make notes while you are watching.

Answer these questions on your own.

▶ 1. What did the woman bring back to the store?

▶ 2. How much did the woman say she had paid for the item?

▶ 3. How long ago had she bought the item?

▶ 4. What did the assistant ask for?

▶ 5. What did the woman say was wrong with the item?

▶ 6. What did the assistant say about the item?

▶ 7. What size was the item?

▶ 8. Why did the assistant want to look at the label?

▶ 9. What make was the woman's tumble-dryer?

▶ 10. What did the woman want the assistant to do?

▶ 11. What did the assistant offer to do?

▶ 12. What do you think the assistant was about to say to the woman at the end of the scene?

Customer care 1

Now form a small group. Discuss these questions and then write down the answers. If you don't all agree – say so.

▶ 13. Describe the woman's attitude and behaviour.

▶ 14. Describe the assistant's attitude and behaviour.

▶ 15. How would you feel if you had to deal with a customer like this?

▶ 16. How well did the assistant deal with the woman? Give examples of things he said or did.

▶ 17. If you were the manager of the store and you witnessed this scene, what would you do?

▶ 18. There is an old saying 'The customer is always right.'

a) What do you think this means?

b) Is the saying correct in this situation?

▶ 19. On a separate piece of paper, write down a list of guidelines for staff to help them to deal with difficult customers.

▶ 20. Many organisations have notices saying how they wish their staff to be treated by customers. Do you think this is a good idea? Does it prevent customers from behaving badly? Does it make the staff feel more secure? On a separate piece of paper, draft out a notice which could be used in this store.

Customer care 2

Watch video clip 9. Make notes while you are watching.

Answer these questions on your own.

▶ 1. What was the name of the garage?

....

▶ 2. What was the mechanic doing when the woman came in?

....

▶ 3. What did the woman think was wrong with her tyre?

....

▶ 4. What make was the woman's car?

....

▶ 5. How long had she owned the car?

....

▶ 6. Which car did the mechanic think was hers?

....

▶ 7. What was the name of the person the mechanic spoke to on his phone?

....

▶ 8. Which tyre did the woman ask the mechanic to look at?

....

▶ 9. How long did the mechanic take to look at her tyres?

....

▶ 10. What did he say was wrong with the tyre she asked him to look at?

....

▶ 11. What did he say was wrong with the other tyres?

....

....

▶ 12. What kind of new tyres did he offer to fit?

....

▶ 13. How much would it have cost to have four of these tyres?

....

▶ 14. At what time did the mechanic tell the woman to call back for her car?

....

Customer care 2

Now form a small group. Discuss these questions and then write down the answers. If you don't all agree – say so.

▶ 15. Describe the mechanic's attitude and behaviour towards the woman.

▶ 16. Give examples of things which the mechanic said or did that you think were wrong. Say why they were wrong.

▶ 17. How do you think the woman was made to feel by the mechanic?

▶ 18. Imagine that you are a close friend of the woman. She has just phoned you to explain what has happened and she is asking for your advice. What would you say to her?

▶ 19. What advice would you give to this woman to help her avoid situations like this in the future?

▶ 20. On a separate piece of paper, write down a set of guidelines for the staff in a garage to help them to provide good service to customers.

Customer care 3

Read this letter, which has been received by the manager of The Quest Hotel in London.

18 Jubilee Grove
Bodbury
Kent
TN7 4DY

23 September

Dear Madam/Sir

I stayed in your hotel on the night of Wednesday 19 September and I am writing to complain about the service I received when I checked out on Thursday 20 September.

I reached the reception desk at 8.30 hoping to check out quickly so that I could catch a train at 9.05 from Euston Station. There was no one else waiting and the two members of staff on duty were talking in the room behind the desk. I rang the bell to attract their attention but this had no immediate effect. After a few minutes a young man who had the name Eric on his badge, came out and said, "We'll be with you in a minute." He then went back and carried on his conversation. At this point I shouted that I was in a hurry and his colleague, Katrina, came out and said, "We are having a computer problem." I told her that I wished to check out. I gave her my name and room number and she said that she would try to work out my bill. She went away and it was ten minutes before she returned with the bill. I read it through and found that I had been over-charged by £56 for an evening meal which I did not have. I pointed this out to Katrina but she said that there was nothing she could do because of the computer problem. At this point, she was joined by Eric, who suggested that I pay and then seek a refund. I refused to do this and asked to see the duty manager. Katrina made a phone call but after five minutes the duty manager had not arrived. I told Eric that I had to leave and suggested that he send the bill to my home address. At no point did either he or Katrina apologise and I would have to say that they were actually quite rude.

Earlier today, the bill arrived in the post and it still showed a charge of £56 for the evening meal. I have no intention of paying this amount but I will, of course, pay for the other items on the bill. Needless to say, I will not stay at your hotel again and will tell my friends and colleagues about the appalling service I received. In the meantime, I would welcome your comments.

Yours faithfully,

Grace Overberry

Grace Overberry

Customer care 3

Work on your own to answer these questions.

▶ 1. Grace was not happy with the service at the Quest Hotel. Make a list of the main things that annoyed her.

▶ 2. Do you think Grace handled the situation well? Give reasons for your answer.

▶ 3. If you had been in her situation, would you have done anything different? If so, explain what you would have done.

▶ 4. Imagine that you are the manager of the Quest Hotel. Think about how to handle this situation. Make a list of the things you intend to do.

▶ 5. On a separate piece of paper, write a reply to Grace explaining what you have done and telling her about anything else you intend to do. Before you start, think about what you hope your letter will achieve.

Phone calls

Listen to audio clip 8.

Answer these questions on your own.

▶ 1. Why was the man phoning the city council?

▶ 2. What was his postcode?

▶ 3. On what days did Sarah-Jane say his bins were due to be emptied?

▶ 4. What difference did it make that there had been a Bank Holiday the week before?

▶ 5. Why do bins have to be placed outside the property in order for them to be emptied?

Now form small groups to discuss and complete these exercises.

▶ 6. Calls to the city council are recorded for training purposes. You are the training manager. If you were speaking to Sarah-Jane about this phone call:

a) How many marks out of ten would you give her?

b) What would you say to her about the way she handled the call?

c) What advice would you give her?

▶ 7. Discuss your answers to question 6. Compare the advice that each of you suggested to Sarah-Jane.

▶ 8. Carry out a short role-play in which you take turns to be Sarah-Jane and the man. Your aim should be to handle his problem in a better way.

▶ 9. Discuss your role-play. Say whether you were able to take your own advice and whether it was good advice.

Satisfied customers

According to 'The UK Customer Satisfaction Index' these ten organisations give the best service to their customers.

1	*John Lewis*	*90.9*
2	*The Fire Service*	*89.8*
3	*Waitrose*	*87.1*
4	*Marks & Spencer Food*	*87.0*
5	*The Ambulance Service*	*86.4*
6	*Mazda*	*86.2*
7	*RAC*	*86.0*
8	*Marks & Spencer Non-Food*	*84.5*
9	*P & O Ferries*	*83.9*
10	*Center Parcs*	*83.8*

These ten organisations give the worst service to their customers.

1	*Local Council*	*55.5*
2	*nPower/RWE*	*59.2*
3	*Jobcentre*	*60.4*
4	*BT*	*61.9*
5	*Local Police*	*63.7*
6	*British Gas*	*64.0*
7	*HM Revenue & Customs*	*64.9*
8	*Talk Talk/Carphone Warehouse*	*65.4*
9	*Stagecoach*	*66.5*
10	*Scottish Power*	*66.9*

All scores are out of 100.

Susan Ward is a business consultant. These are her eight rules for good customer service:

- Answer your phone.
- Don't make promises unless you **will** keep them.
- Listen to your customers.
- Deal with complaints.
- Be helpful – even if there's no immediate profit in it.
- Train staff to **always** be helpful, courteous and knowledgeable.
- Take the extra step.
- Throw in something extra.

Answer these questions on your own.

▶ 1. **Which organisation gave the best customer service?**

....

▶ 2. **Which organisation gave the worst customer service?**

....

Satisfied customers

▶ 3. List the organisations from both tables that you have had dealings with.

....

....

....

▶ 4. Choose two of those organisations and describe the customer service you received. Give them your own mark out of 100.

Organisation	*Experience*	*Mark*

Now work in a small group. Imagine that you run a small business. Discuss these questions and write down your answers. If you don't all agree – say so.

▶ 5. Look at Susan Ward's rules for good customer service. Choose the three that you think are most important.

....

....

....

▶ 6. What does Susan Ward mean when she says, "Be helpful – even if there's no immediate profit in it"?

....

....

....

Satisfied customers

▶ 7. Give examples of what it means to:

Take the extra step

Throw in something extra

▶ 8. How can a company benefit from providing good customer service?

▶ 9. Draw up your own 'Rules for good customer service'. You can include some of Susan Ward's but make up some of your own too.

1	
2	
3	
4	
5	
6	
7	
8	
9	
10	

Help!

Listen to audio clips 9a-d. Make notes while you are listening.

Working on your own, answer these questions about the four 999 calls. In each case, imagine that you are the operator receiving the call.

Audio clip 9a

▶ 1. Is the call genuine or a hoax? Give reasons for your answer.

▶ 2. What would you say to the caller? For example, would you give them any advice?

▶ 3. What further information would you ask the caller to give you?

Audio clip 9b

▶ 4. Is the call genuine or a hoax? Give reasons for your answer.

▶ 5. What would you say to the caller? For example, would you give them any advice?

▶ 6. What further information would you ask the caller to give you?

Audio clip 9c

▶ 7. Is the call genuine or a hoax? Give reasons for your answer.

Help!

▶ 8. What would you say to the caller? For example, would you give them any advice?

▶ 9. What further information would you ask the caller to give you?

Audio clip 9d

▶ 10. Is the call genuine or a hoax? Give reasons for your answer.

▶ 11. What would you say to the caller? For example, would you give them any advice?

▶ 12. What further information would you ask the caller to give you?

Work in small groups.

▶ 13. Choose one of the four phone calls. Devise a role-play in which the conversation between the operator and the caller is continued. The people who are not involved should give their opinions on the role-play when it is finished.

▶ 14. Choose another one of the four phone calls. Devise a role-play with different members of the group playing the parts.

▶ 15. Take turns to perform one of your role-plays for the whole class.

▶ 16. Discuss the role-plays and how each situation was handled. Then, on a separate piece of paper, draw up a list of guidelines for emergency call operators.

▶ 17. Next, draw up a list of guidelines for anyone who has to make a 999 call.

The boss blunders

You work at 'The Pizza Place'. The manager, Mario, has designed a flyer and printed 1,000 copies. He wants you to deliver them door-to-door around the local area.

The Pizza Place

14 High Street. Telefone: 0114 326 4414

Opening Monday 12 Febuary. Under new mangement.

Open dailey 12 noon – 12 midnite.

Free delivry (For orders of £8 and over within a 4 mile distance)

Cash or Card only. No checks excepted.

The widest range of pizza's in town. All made from natural ingreedient's.

Special opening weak offer: Buy any Piza and drink and get drunk free!

Choose from 10 inch, 12 inch and 14 inch.

Try our Valentine's Day Special: Two 12 inch pizzas plus galric bread only £12

'It's the best cusuine in town right here. Authetnic Italian - Mamma Mia!'

You can see that there are lots of mistakes on the flyer. Mario is not very good at spelling and punctuation and his keyboard skills are poor. His graphics are also pretty bad.

▶ 1. What is the purpose of a flyer?

....

▶ 2. What makes a flyer effective?

....

....

▶ 3. Draw a circle round each incorrect spelling or punctuation on Mario's flyer.

The boss blunders

▶ 4. In the table below write down all the mistakes and correct them.

Mistakes	*Corrections*	*Mistakes*	*Corrections*

▶ 5. What would happen if you delivered the flyers with all these mistakes in them?

▶ 6. How can you tell Mario what you think of his flyer? Think about it first and write down three possible things that you could say to him. It's probably not a good idea to say, "Hey Mario, those flyers are rubbish."!

▶ 7. On a separate piece of paper, re-design the flyer with all the mistakes corrected and the graphics and layout improved.

▶ 8. Display all the flyers produced by the members of the class. Look at them, discuss them and then choose the three most effective designs.

A phone call from the boss

Listen to audio clip 10.

Answer these questions on your own.

▶ 1. What was the name of the person making the call?

▶ 2. Where was she calling from?

▶ 3. What was her new flight number?

▶ 4. Where was it due to arrive?

▶ 5. At what time was it due to arrive?

▶ 6. At what time was she due to meet Barbara?

▶ 7. Where was this meeting?

▶ 8. At what time were they supposed to be meeting the clients?

▶ 9. What information did she ask you to pass on to Barbara?

Now work in a small group to carry out these tasks.

▶ 10. Make a list of the jobs you have to do.

A phone call from the boss

▶ 11. Place these jobs in order of priority (the important ones first).

▶ 12. Next to each job, write down how long you think it will take.

▶ 13. As it happens, you haven't got Barbara's mobile number. What can you do?

▶ 14. What problems or questions might you need to sort out – either with Barbara or on your own?

▶ 15. Now, be honest and describe your feelings when you were listening to the phone call from your boss.

▶ 16. Did you manage to grab a pen and make notes? If so, how good were your notes? If not, how much were you able to remember?

▶ 17. Do you think your boss would be happy with the way you dealt with things? Give reasons for your answer.

▶ 18. Act out or write a short script or story in which the boss is talking to you the next day about how well you did.

▶ 19. If you had to deal with something like this again, what, if anything, would you do differently? Say why you would do things differently. Write your ideas on a separate sheet of paper.

When things go wrong

You work in a small restaurant. Each day you arrive for work at 11 am to prepare for opening at 12 noon. This morning you find a note from the owner.

Taken mother-in-law to hospital. You are in charge until I get back. Chef will be late. Wine stock seems low – contact suppliers if necessary. Check if heating is working – seemed cold last night. Dishwasher needs emptying. Cleaner hasn't been in so far this morning and toilets are in a bit of a state from last night. Party of nine people coming in at 12.30 but I forgot to put it in the book. Should be okay. Expecting electrician at 1 pm to discuss prices for new light fittings. Call or text me if you really need to. I'm sure you'll be okay.

How would you cope with this situation?

▶ 1. **What are your first thoughts?**

▶ 2. **In the first column of the table below make a list of all the jobs you will have to do.**

▶ 3. **In the second column give each job a priority number. The job you will need to do first should be given the number 1 and so on.**

Jobs	***Priority***

▶ 4. **Under what circumstances, if any, would you contact the owner?**

When things go wrong

You are arranging a surprise party for the boss of your company to celebrate 25 years in business. She thinks that you are taking her for a quiet meal with all the managers but you have made the following plans:

- Room booked at a hotel in town for a four-course meal.
- Arriving at 7.30 pm for drinks. Meal served at 8 pm. Disco and dancing until 12 pm.
- One hundred employees and colleagues have been invited.
- Transport by stretch limo, arriving at boss's house at 7 pm.
- Co-director from Australia arriving at 6.45 pm.
- Boss to be presented with tickets for a holiday which has been paid for by the board.

During the course of the day a number of problems arise. Your teacher will read them out to you. In the spaces below write down how you would deal with each problem when you hear about it.

Problems

How you would deal with them?

▶ 1. ....

....

....

....

▶ 2. ....

....

....

....

▶ 3. ....

....

....

....

▶ 4. ....

....

....

....

When things go wrong

▶ 5.

▶ 6.

▶ 7.

▶ 8.

Eyewitness

Chloe is a community police officer. As part of her job she has to take statements from witnesses. Some witnesses are not very good at remembering what they saw. Here is a conversation Chloe had with a witness to an attempted robbery.

Chloe:	So you were in the shop when the men came in?
Witness:	Yes. Well, sort of. I was like, coming in I think.
Chloe:	And how many men were there?
Witness:	Two, I think.
Chloe:	And what did they look like?
Witness:	One was taller than the other. The second man was a bit shorter.
Chloe:	Did you notice anything else about them – were they white or black?
Witness:	Yes, they could have been.
Chloe:	Could have been what?
Witness:	White or black.
Chloe:	What were they wearing?
Witness:	I think one of them had jeans on and a hood and the other one had a hat. But I can't remember what else they were wearing.
Chloe:	And what did they do when they came in the shop?
Witness:	I think one of them went up to the man behind the counter and the other one sort of just stood there.
Chloe:	What happened next?
Witness:	I think he pulled something out of his pocket.
Chloe:	Who did?
Witness:	The first one, the one at the counter.
Chloe:	What did he pull out of his pocket?
Witness:	I think it was a gun.
Chloe:	Did you get a good look at it?
Witness:	No! I was terrified. I just screamed and then I shouted, "He's got a gun!"
Chloe:	And what happened then?
Witness:	I hid behind the toilet rolls and that's when they ran away.
Chloe:	Did you see them run away?
Witness:	No, but I heard one of them say, "I'm getting off," and then I heard them running. I stayed behind the toilet rolls.

This witness didn't make Chloe's job any easier. Would you be any better?

Eyewitness

Watch video clips 10a and b. Make notes while you are watching each one.

▶ 1. Fill in these reports after you have watched the clips.

Eyewitness report
Description of location
Number of people involved
Description of people involved
What you saw

Eyewitness report
Description of location
Number of people involved
Description of people involved
What you saw

Eyewitness

▶ 2. Now compare your reports with those of other people in the class. Were they similar? If not, how different were they?

▶ 3. Look at the video clips again. What, if anything, did you fail to see or remember?

▶ 4. What can you do to improve your ability to remember things you see?

▶ 5. Name some situations in different jobs where it is important to remember accurately what you have seen.

▶ 6. Work with a partner. Carry out a short role-play in which you take turns to be a community police officer and a witness to what has happened in the two video clips.

Every picture tells a story

When we are working we don't always have time to see exactly what is going on around us. We often see people in different situations but usually only for a second or two. Then, without thinking about it, we form opinions about these people based on what we see.

Look at stills clips 1a–d. Work in small groups.

▶ 1. Discuss each of the pictures in turn. You might want to start by asking questions. For example:

- What do you know about the people in the pictures?
- What can you guess about them?
- What is happening?
- What happened before the picture was taken?
- What are the 'clues' that tell you what is going on in the pictures?

▶ 2. Write down the main things you all agree about in each picture.

....

....

....

▶ 3. Write down some of the things you disagree about in each picture.

....

....

....

▶ 4. As a class, discuss the pictures one at a time and compare what each group has written about them.

▶ 5. Does a picture tell the same story to everybody who sees it? Explain your answer.

....

....

....

▶ 6. Choose one of the pictures and explain how two people could form totally different opinions about what is going on.

....

....

....

▶ 7. How could this be a problem in a work situation?

....

....

Body language 1

When you start a new job one of the main things you worry about is the people you will be working with. What will they be like? How will they treat you? Will you get on with them?

Look at stills clips 2a–d. Answer these questions about each picture on your own.

Stills clip 2a

▶ 1. Write down the first three words which come to mind when you look at this person.

▶ 2. If you met this person, what would you think? Tick one of these boxes.

I would immediately like them.	
I might get to like them.	
I probably wouldn't get to like them.	
I would immediately dislike them.	

▶ 3. Would you feel happy about working with this person? Give reasons for your answer.

▶ 4. If you were introduced to this person at a party, what would you do or say? Again, give reasons for your answers.

▶ 5. List three things about their appearance or body language that gave you these opinions about them.

Stills clip 2b

▶ 6. Write down the first three words which come to mind when you look at this person.

Body language 1

▶ 7. If you met this person, what would you think? Tick one of these boxes.

I would immediately like them.	
I might get to like them.	
I probably wouldn't get to like them.	
I would immediately dislike them.	

▶ 8. Would you feel happy about working with this person? Give reasons for your answer.

....

....

▶ 9. If you were introduced to this person at a party, what would you do or say? Again, give reasons for your answers.

....

....

▶ 10. List three things about their appearance or body language that gave you these opinions about them.

....

....

....

Stills clip 2c

▶ 11. Write down the first three words which come to your mind when you look at this person.

....

▶ 12. If you met this person, what would you think? Tick one of these boxes.

I would immediately like them.	
I might get to like them.	
I probably wouldn't get to like them.	
I would immediately dislike them.	

▶ 13. Would you feel happy about working with this person? Give reasons for your answer.

....

....

Body language 1

▶ 14. If you were introduced to this person at a party, what would you do or say? Again, give reasons for your answers.

▶ 15. List three things about their appearance or body language that gave you these opinions about them.

Stills clip 2d

▶ 16. Write down the first three words which come to your mind when you look at this person.

▶ 17. If you met this person, what would you think? Tick one of these boxes.

I would immediately like them.	
I might get to like them.	
I probably wouldn't get to like them.	
I would immediately dislike them.	

▶ 18. Would you feel happy about working with this person? Give reasons for your answer.

▶ 19. If you were introduced to this person at a party, what would you do or say? Again, give reasons for your answers.

▶ 20. List three things about their appearance or body language that gave you these opinions about them.

Body language 1

Discuss your answers as a whole class.

▶ 21. Did you all have similar opinions about the four people or did you disagree?

▶ 22. Add up the class totals for each of the possible answers to questions 2, 7, 12 and 17 and fill them in below.

Stills clip 2a	***Class totals***
I would immediately like them.	
I might get to like them.	
I probably wouldn't get to like them.	
I would immediately dislike them.	

Stills clip 2b	***Class totals***
I would immediately like them.	
I might get to like them.	
I probably wouldn't get to like them.	
I would immediately dislike them.	

Stills clip 2c	***Class totals***
I would immediately like them.	
I might get to like them.	
I probably wouldn't get to like them.	
I would immediately dislike them.	

Stills clip 2d	***Class totals***
I would immediately like them.	
I might get to like them.	
I probably wouldn't get to like them.	
I would immediately dislike them.	

▶ 23. All of these opinions were made after looking at one still picture. What does this tell you about the importance of body language?

Body language 2

Look at video clips 11a–d.

Form small groups and discuss each of the situations in turn. You can look at them again if you wish. Then answer these questions. If you don't all agree – say so.

Video clip 11a – This is a work situation. Ron is the person standing. Don is the person sitting.

▶ 1. Who is the boss? How do you know?

▶ 2. What is Ron doing?

▶ 3. How would you feel if you were Don? Explain why you would feel like this.

▶ 4. Make a list of things about Ron's body language that you didn't like. Say why you didn't like them.

▶ 5. If Ron were your boss what would you do or say?

Video clip 11b – These two people work at the same place. They are on their way home after a hard day. Rita is the talkative one. The other person is Anita.

▶ 6. How would you feel if you were Anita? Explain why you would feel like this.

▶ 7. Make a list of things about Rita's body language that you didn't like. Say why you didn't like them.

Body language 2

▶ 8. Make a list of things about Rita's body language that you **did** like. Say why you liked them.

▶ 9. In what ways did Anita's body language show what she felt about Rita?

▶ 10. What advice would you give to Anita about Rita?

▶ 11. How would you feel if you worked with Rita?

Video clip 11c – This is an office party. The man's name is Benny. The woman is Jenny.

▶ 12. What does Benny think about Jenny? Explain how you know this.

▶ 13. What does Jenny think about Benny? Explain how you know this.

▶ 14. Make a list of things about Benny's body language that Jenny didn't like. Explain why she didn't like them.

▶ 15. What does Benny's body language tell you about his self-image? Explain your answer.

Body language 2

▶ 16. What does Jenny's body language tell you about her self-image? Explain your answer.

▶ 17. Benny is not Jenny's boss. What does his body language tell you about his attitude to her?

▶ 18. You are Jenny's friend. She asks your advice. How can she handle Benny's behaviour at work?

Video clip 11d – Ann has an interview but she can't find the office block where the interview is being held. The map she has been given is not very clear. Can Stan help?

▶ 19. What did Stan think when he first saw Ann? Explain how you know this.

▶ 20. Why did Stan walk past and then go back to Ann?

▶ 21. How do you think Ann felt about Stan offering to help her? Give reasons for your answer.

▶ 22. How did Stan make Ann feel good about herself when he was helping her?

▶ 23. If you had been a passer-by, what would you have thought about Ann and Stan?

Body language 2

▶ 24. Would Stan and Ann be good people to work with? Give reasons for your answer.

▶ 25. Take each of the four situations in turn and discuss them as a class. Compare the opinions of the different groups.

▶ 26. Who had the 'best' body language? Who had the 'worst' body language? Take a class vote.

Best body language	***Votes***
Ron	
Don	
Rita	
Anita	
Jenny	
Benny	
Ann	
Stan	

Worst body language	***Votes***
Ron	
Don	
Rita	
Anita	
Jenny	
Benny	
Ann	
Stan	

Stranded

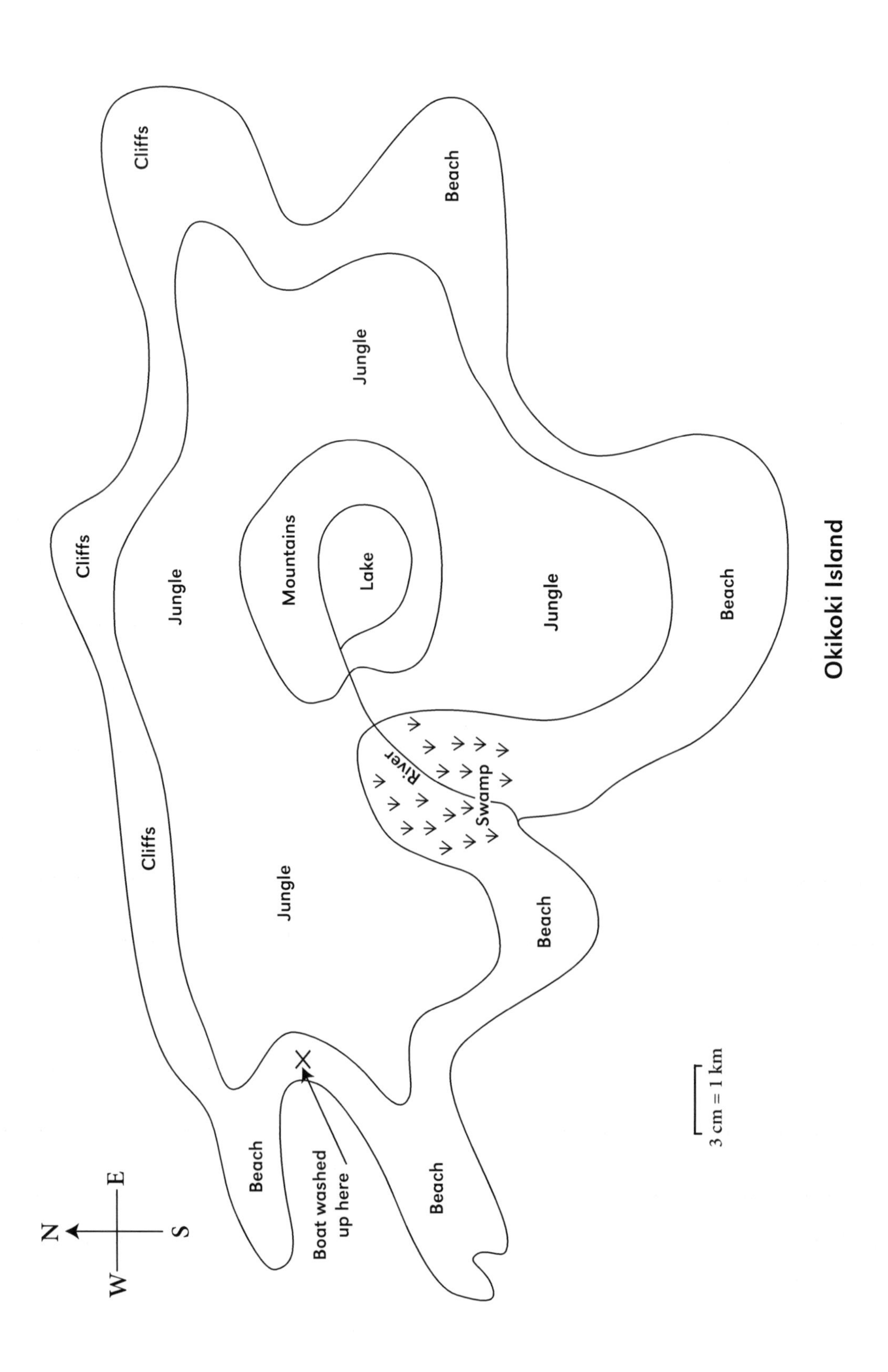
Cliffs
Beach
Jungle
Cliffs
Jungle
Mountains
Lake
Jungle
Beach
Okikoki Island
River
Swamp
Cliffs
Jungle
Beach
Boat washed up here
Beach
Beach
3 cm = 1 km
N
E
S
W

Stranded

As part of your training in your new job you are taking part in a team-building exercise. Carry out this exercise in a group of 4–6 people. You will be given a map.

You are sailing in the Pacific Ocean with a group of friends when your boat suddenly begins to sink. You have no radio, but luckily you are only a few kilometres from Okikoki Island and you are washed ashore on an empty beach. The boat has broken up and only a few pieces of wood and a sail are left. Then you see a wooden box. You open it and find the following items:

Two long ropes, a wind-up torch, a compass, six flares, fourteen litres of drinking water, an axe, a saw, a pencil, a notebook, a map of Okikoki Island

You realise that you need to stay safe and healthy until you can be rescued. What are you going to do? Read through these questions. Discuss them, and try to agree on the answers. There is no time to waste on arguing.

▶ 1. **Draw up a list of things you need to do immediately. Here are some suggestions to start you off.**

Move everything off the beach
Check for injuries

▶ 2. **Look at the map and decide where you should set up camp. Say why you have chosen this site.**

....

....

Stranded

▶ 3. How long do you think it will take you to reach this site?

▶ 4. Describe the route you will take.

▶ 5. What are the possible dangers on the island?

▶ 6. How long do you think your drinking water will last?

▶ 7. How could you obtain fresh drinking water?

▶ 8. How could you obtain food?

▶ 9. You have six flares. When would be the best time to use them?

▶ 10. How could you build a shelter?

▶ 11. The island is uninhabited. The nearest island with people is over 20 kilometres away to the south east. It is not a good idea just to wait and see if anyone comes looking for you. What could you do to help your chances of being rescued?

▶ 12. It is one year later and you are back home safe and well. On a separate piece of paper, write the story of how you survived and how you were rescued.

Assessment and evaluation

In this exercise you are going to assess the progress you think you have made. Please try to answer these questions as honestly as you can – even if some of them seem difficult.

Name:

1. After following this course of study, what do you think is meant by *Thinking Skills for Work*?
2. Why do you think it is important for people to have good *Thinking Skills for Work*?
3. How much had you thought about these abilities before starting this course of study?
4. Describe a situation where you have been affected or concerned by your lack of thinking skills in work situations.

Refer to the checklist which your teacher has given you to help you to answer the rest of the questions.

5. Which topics or activities have you most enjoyed during your work on these issues?
6. Which topics or activities have you found least enjoyable?
7. Which topics or activities have you found most useful?
8. Which topics have you found least useful?
9. How much do you think you have benefited from taking part in this work?
10. What other similar topics do you think are important and should be included in your studies?

▶ 11. Based on your answers to these questions, draw up an action plan designed to help you to improve your *Thinking Skills for Work*.

Checklist

Section	*Topic*	*Covered*	*Comments*
Getting a job/wages	*Jobs 1*		
	Jobs 2		
	Interview 1		
	Interview 2		
	Interview 3		
	Just the job?		
	Wages		
	A fair wage?		
	Talking		
	Literacy levels at work		
Training	*Magic*		
	Menu		
	Following instructions – know your napkins		
	Following instructions – serviette style		
	Darts		
On the job	*Introducing Z Factor*		
	Finish the lyrics		
	Breaking news		
	News headlines		
	Picture this		
	Picture that		
	Picture these		
	The Daily Blag		

Checklist

Section	Topic	Covered	Comments
On the job (continued)	Pedalo power		
	The fishing line		
	Public speaking		
	Speaking in public		
	Listen carefully		
Customer care	Customer care 1		
	Customer care 2		
	Customer care 3		
	Phone calls		
	Satisfied customers		
	Help!		
Work problems and relationships	The boss blunders		
	A phone call from the boss		
	When things go wrong		
	Eyewitness		
	Every picture tells a story		
	Body language 1		
	Body language 2		
	Stranded		

Teacher's notes and answers

Jobs 1, pages 9–11

Aims

Students will:

- read and understand job advertisements
- extract the important pieces of information from the advertisements
- make basic mathematical calculations involving the figures included in the job descriptions
- assess their aptitudes for each job
- understand the use of fictional situations in developing transferable skills.

Teaching points

You should begin by explaining that this is intended to be a bit of fun and that the jobs are not realistic. However, you should emphasise that this lesson will encourage a creative approach to students' work and develop self-confidence and other transferable skills.

Less able students might need help in reading the advertisements. They might find some of the words and phrases in the advertisements difficult to understand. You should explain that these are used frequently and need to be understood.

As an extension activity you could ask each student in turn to say which job they would most like to apply for and why. This could lead on to a whole-class discussion about aptitudes for certain areas of employment.

Answers

1. 'On-the-job training' is training given while you are actually doing the job as opposed to training off the job (at a college, for example).
2. Free life insurance is provided because the jobs are potentially dangerous.
3. You would earn £230 per week in these jobs.
4. People who might not be able to do this job include old people and people with disabilities.
5. 'CV' stands for Curriculum Vitae. It is a Latin term that means the path of your life.
6. 'Initially' means to start with or in the beginning. So 'three days a week initially' means you would begin with working three days a week, but it might increase.
7. The 'good communication skills' are probably needed more for interaction with the customers who own the dogs.
8. You would earn £156.
9. A 'CV' is a list or account of your relevant experience, qualities, aptitude, interests and qualifications.
10. 'Cover for maternity leave' means you would be working to cover the job of someone who has taken time off to have a baby.
11. An 'affinity' is a liking or attraction.
12. 'Good hand-eye coordination' means being able to see things clearly and to react using your hands in an appropriate way without being clumsy. Key cutting is an intricate job so having this ability would be an advantage.
13. 'Opportunity for position to be made permanent dependent on performance' means if you do well in the job you might be taken on permanently.
14. The approximate annual salary for this job is £12,400.
15. 'Positive discrimination' means providing opportunities and facilities, where necessary, for people from specific backgrounds and encouraging them to apply for jobs.
16. Senior citizens are people over the age of 60.
17. An 'induction period' is a period when you are regarded as learning the job and usually when you are receiving training, guidance and supervision. There is usually a review at the end of this period before the job is made permanent.
18. 'Six-day, two-shift system, alternating each week' means you work six days a week. There are different shifts or working times. You work one shift for one week and the other shift the next week, and so on.
19. In this job you would earn £64 each day.
20. One of the perks of this job is the free visits to the Grotto for members of your family.
21. You are probably asked to include a recent photograph in your application so the company can see if you have a pleasant face and could be made to look like a realistic elf.

Teacher's notes and answers

Jobs 2, page 12

Aims

Students will:

- make an individual assessment of a letter of application
- write a letter of application
- work cooperatively to assess letters of application from others in the class
- understand the use of fictional situations in developing transferable skills.

Teaching points

You should begin by explaining that this is intended to be a bit of fun and that the jobs are not realistic. However, you should emphasise that this lesson will encourage a creative approach to students' work and develop self-confidence and other transferable skills.

You should analyse Shirley's letter as part of a whole-class discussion. Less able students might need help with all aspects of this lesson. You can allow students to form their own groups or you might prefer to place them in groups with an appropriate social and academic mix. The latter approach will, of course, need to be carried out sensitively. The final part of the lesson should be carried out in a positive and supportive manner, so that less able students do not have their shortcomings highlighted in front of others. If pupils do not wish their letters of application to be read by others their wishes should be respected.

Interview 1, pages 13–14

Aims

Students will:

- concentrate on a visual and oral record of social interaction during job interviews
- recall relevant observations from a social interaction
- analyse observed behaviour
- communicate and discuss opinions of observed behaviour
- make conclusions based on observations and subsequent discussions
- carry out research.

Preparation and resources

You will need the Thinking skills for work CD, computer/s and/or an interactive white board. You should also provide internet access so students can research information relevant to the job of hotel porter.

Teaching points

You can allow students to form their own groups or you might prefer to place them in groups with an appropriate social and academic mix. The latter approach will, of course, need to be carried out sensitively.

You should emphasise that hotel porters can be female as well as male.

At the end of the task, you should ask each group to present their conclusions to the rest of the class in turn.

Answers

1. A hotel porter liaises with the hotel reception team and ensures that the hotel guests' comfort, satisfaction and wellbeing are catered for in a friendly, helpful and personalised manner at all times. This involves handling luggage but could also require giving information, taking messages, parking cars, obtaining taxis, taking meals, laundry and other items to and from rooms.
2. You do not need any qualifications to be a hotel porter, although employers will usually expect you to have a good general education and communication skills. You may have an advantage when looking for work if you have experience of working with the public. You will need a full driving licence if your job involves parking guests' cars. Knowledge of the local area will be useful, so that you can answer guests' questions and give them directions. You may be able to get into this job through an apprenticeship scheme. The range of apprenticeships available in your area will depend on the local job market and the types of skills employers need from their workers.

Teacher's notes and answers

Once you start work you will usually receive on-the-job training from experienced staff. You may also be able to work towards qualifications such as: NVQ Level 1 in Hospitality and NVQ Level 2 in Multi-Skilled Hospitality Services.

Interview 2, pages 15–16

Aims

Students will:

- concentrate on a visual and oral record of social interaction during job interviews
- recall relevant observations from a social interaction
- analyse observed behaviour
- communicate and discuss opinions of the observed behaviour
- make conclusions based on observations and subsequent discussions
- carry out research.

Preparation and resources

You will need the Thinking skills for work CD, computer/s and/or an interactive white board.
You should also provide internet access so students can research information relevant to the qualities and skills needed to be a good interviewer.

Teaching points

You can allow students to form their own groups or you might prefer to place them in groups with an appropriate social and academic mix. The latter approach will, of course, need to be carried out sensitively.

You should emphasise that hotel porters can be female as well as male.

At the end of the task, you should ask each group to present their conclusions to the rest of the class in turn.

Answers

1. Amongst other things, a good interviewer should:
    - be a good communicator
    - be well-prepared
    - be organised
    - understand the needs of the job
    - fit the correct person to the job
    - be able to put people at ease and allow them to show themselves at their best
    - understand legal issues relating to employment, such as discrimination
    - provide information about the job
    - explore the potential of candidates without asking over-personal questions.

Interview 3, pages 17–19

Aims

Students will:

- concentrate on a visual and oral record of social interaction during job interviews
- recall relevant observations from a social interaction
- analyse observed behaviour
- communicate and discuss opinions of the observed behaviour
- make conclusions based on observations and subsequent discussions
- carry out research.

Preparation and resources

You will need the Thinking skills for work CD, computer/s and/or an interactive white board.

Teaching points

You can allow students to form their own groups or you might prefer to place them in groups with an appropriate social and academic mix. The latter approach will, of course, need to be carried out sensitively.

You should emphasise that hotel porters can be female as well as male.

At the end of the task, you should ask each group to present their conclusions to the rest of the class in turn. This should be followed by a plenary session in which all the relevant issues are discussed. Any generally agreed conclusions should be recorded.

Teacher's notes and answers

Just the job?, pages 20–26

Aims

Students will:

- read and understand examples of text which contain numerical information and are in the form of a series of job advertisements
- answer questions relating to the text
- make calculations based on the numerical information in the text
- make deductions about the working conditions in the jobs by analysing the information
- match up own skills, qualities and preferences to each of the jobs
- draft a letter of application for one of the jobs.

Preparation and resources

You may need to provide dictionaries, atlases, calculators and access to the internet for this task.

Teaching points

These job advertisements are genuine and each of them was advertised in local or national newspapers during 2009. In some cases, the name of the company or firm and other information irrelevant to this exercise has been left out.

You should explain that although some of these jobs would not be suitable for your students because they lack the experience and qualifications, they have been included to give them an idea of the range of opportunities which exist and also, to encourage them to aspire to things which they might not have considered at this stage in their lives.

With less able students you should read at least some of the job specifications aloud and discuss any parts they find difficult to understand. Students should write out their answers working on their own. They may need to research the answers to some of the questions on the internet. You could cover the answers to the questions as part of a whole-class discussion, perhaps asking for answers to be read out by volunteers. Volunteers could take turns to read out their letters of application and these could be discussed in a supportive way as part of a final plenary session.

Answers

1. 'Hours: Not specified' means there are no details of the times you would be expected to work.
2. The approximate weekly wage for this job is £300.
6. A bonus is extra money that is usually paid as a result of good performance in the job.
7. A retailer is a business that sells to the public, usually a shop.
11. You would earn between £240–£288 if you worked eight hours a day, three days a week.
14. £60K–£70K
16. There are no qualifications specified for this job.
17. Personal qualities needed for this job include flexibility, humour and willingness to go the extra mile.
18. Duties in this job would include supporting the learning of the students under the direction of the teacher.
19. Working at a residential school might mean you have to work overnight and at weekends.
21. £237
22. The job is based in Cambridge.
23. The Antarctic is the South Pole.
24. Problems with travelling and working in the Antarctic include the fact that it's cold, you would be working away from friends and family, there would be a long distance to travel, you would be working in close contact with other people, there would be long, dark winters.
25. £1,150
26. Qualifications needed for this job include: NVQ Level 1 (or equivalent) together with reception/switchboard experience, RSA Level 1 typing and a working knowledge of Microsoft 2003.
29. £294
30. As an advertising telesales representative you would be making phone calls to try to sell advertising space.
31. Cold calls are calls to people who haven't asked you to phone them, aren't expecting you to call them and might not want you to call them.
33. £288

Teacher's notes and answers

36. £250
37. No qualifications are specified for this job.
38. The Falkland Islands are 300 miles off the coast of Argentina and 8,000 miles away from Britain.
39. If you took the job, your family would either have to live on their own in Britain or move to live with you in the Falkland Islands.
40. The particular challenges of the Falklands include the fact that the Falkland Islands are isolated, Argentina still has ambitions to take it over from British rule and it has little or no natural resources. The main sources of income are sheep farming, fishing and tourism. The population is small and spread over a large area.
41. £100,000
44. 'This represents a unique opportunity for the right candidate to get in at the ground floor' means you will learn a lot from the experience of working for a company that is just starting up.
45. £346

Wages, pages 27–28

Aims

Students will:

- read and understand text containing numerical information in the form of a payslip
- answer questions relating to the information
- make calculations based on the numerical information in the text
- carry out relevant research into the topics of income tax and National Insurance
- devise a role-play from which useful information can be gained about handling pay-related situations in work.

Preparation and resources

You will need access to the internet so students can research about income tax and National Insurance. Government pamphlets or information sheets may also come in handy.

Teaching points

You should allow students to research information relating to income tax and National Insurance. You could allow them to have access to the internet or you could provide information in the form of government pamphlets and information sheets.

For the role-play you can allow students to choose their own partners or you could place them in pairs which you think would be suitable. The latter approach will have to be carried out sensitively. The role-plays could be discussed in a constructive and supportive manner and used to suggest ideas for the final part of the lesson. All students should be encouraged to take part in the role-play but if any of them find it too difficult, they could observe other pairs and take notes. Alternatively, they can go straight on to the final part of the lesson. The completed lists and leaflets could be displayed and discussed in a final session.

Answers

1. £225.40
2. The term 'Net pay' is used to describe the amount of money Jay actually got paid.
3. Deductions are the amounts of money taken out of the pay before the person receives it. They include income tax and National Insurance.
4. Tax, in this case, is income tax. This is money taken out of the wages and paid to the government who use it to run the country. Taxes pay for the services we receive. The amount of income tax you pay depends on the amount you earn. The more you earn the more you pay.
5. National Insurance is the money you pay to fund Social Security benefits including the provision of your state pension. The amount you pay in National Insurance also increases according to how much you earn.
6. A tax code is a figure that shows how much tax you should pay. It is worked out according to a number of factors, including your earnings, other sources of income and your circumstances, such as whether you have children or other people who depend on you.

Teacher's notes and answers

7. These are the mistakes:

1	*The employee's name is spelt incorrectly. It is shown as McGinly instead of McGinty.*
2	*The employee's payment figure is incorrect. 40 hours at £8.50 per hour should = £340.*
3	*The employee's net pay is incorrect. According to the figure given, he should have received only £223.40. This is an over-payment of £2.* *However, using the correct figure for his payment and subtracting the deductions as listed, he should have received £243.40. This is an under-payment of £18.* *(More able students should be able to work out the two calculations but less able students might only be able to work out the mistake based on the figures on the payslip.)*
4	*February is spelt incorrectly as Febuary.*

A fair wage?, pages 29–30

Aims

Students will:

- read, understand and analyse text containing statistics relating to money
- answer questions based on the statistics
- increase awareness of issues relating to wages
- work with others to consider some of the issues relating to the exceedingly high wages paid to some people in modern society.

Preparation and resources

You will need to provide calculators for this activity.

Teaching points

The figures relating to the wages and other payments are estimates reported in *The Times* on 12 June 2009.

With less able students you might need to read through the statistical information and explain some of the data. You can allow the use of calculators. You should go through the answers to questions 1–10 before asking students to working on questions 11 and 12. You can allow students to form their own pairs or you might prefer to place each of them with an appropriate partner. The latter approach will, of course, need to be carried out sensitively. You could ask for volunteers to perform their interviews as role-plays for the rest of the class.

Answers

1. The young man's name was Ronaldo.
2. Ronaldo was a footballer.
3. £25,000
4. Over 4 years (4.8 years)
5. Nike and Castrol paid Ronaldo money to advertise and endorse their products.
6. £14.2 m
7. £182,000
8. £555,000
9. Five hundred and fifty-five thousand pounds.
10. 3,200

Talking, page 31

Aims

Students will:

- listen to, analyse and make judgements about communication skills as demonstrated by a range of people in an audio clip
- compare and discuss opinions on communication skills with others
- assess the communication skills needed for a particular job.

Preparation and resources

You will need the Thinking skills for work CD, computer/s and/or an interactive white board.

Teaching points

You can allow students to form their own groups or you might prefer to place them in groups with an appropriate social and academic mix. The latter approach will, of course, need to be carried out sensitively.

Teacher's notes and answers

Group discussion should be carried out in a constructive and supportive manner.

For the final task there are two possible approaches:

- you could count how many groups awarded the job to each presenter
- you could add together the scores from each group for each of the four presenters.

It would be interesting to try both methods to see if they give different results.

Literacy levels at work, pages 32–34

Aims

Students will:

- read, understand and analyse text containing statistics relating to levels of literacy
- answer questions based on the statistics
- increase their awareness of issues relating to levels of literacy
- work with others to consider ways in which levels of literacy can be raised
- reflect on their own levels of literacy.

Preparation and resources

You will need to make dictionaries and calculators available for this activity.

Teaching points

Figures for England: DfES 2003

Figures for Wales: Basic Skills Agency 2005

Figures for N. Ireland: International Adult Literacy Survey 1998

Figures for Scotland: Scottish Executive 2001

With less able students you might need to read through the statistical information and explain some of the data. You can allow the use of calculators. You should go through the answers to questions 1–8 before asking students to work on questions 9 and 10. You can allow students to form their own groups or you might prefer to place them in groups with an appropriate social and academic mix. The latter approach will, of course, need to be carried out sensitively. Questions 9 and 10 can be answered on separate pieces of paper.

You could ask for volunteers to perform the phone-in as a role-play to the rest of the class. Questions 11 and 12 should be handled very sensitively and students should understand that their answers will be treated as confidential unless they volunteer to discuss them.

Answers

1. Literacy is the ability to read and write.

2. If someone is illiterate it means they cannot read or write.

3. There are not many people in Britain who are completely illiterate.

4. Working age is from 16–65 years old.

5. 16% of the working population in England was in the low skills category (at entry level 3 or below).

6. and 7. Students will make their own choices but they should show understanding and logic in their opinions.

8. There are signs of improvement. Since 2001 the number of adults in the workforce without level 2 has reduced from 7.1 million to 6.8 million.

9. Answers should show understanding and logic and should address the points made by Ernie. The use of humour in this question should be allowed or even encouraged.

10. Posters/flyers should be well designed, and conform to the students' stated aims. Text and artwork should be simple but effective.

Magic, page 35

Aims

Students will:

- concentrate on a visual demonstration of magic tricks
- analyse the skills demonstrated in performing the tricks
- propose and test hypotheses to explain how the tricks are done
- communicate their hypotheses to others and invite comment and criticism
- modify their hypotheses in the light of comment and criticism.

Teacher's notes and answers

These aims relate to magic tricks, but they represent transferable skills that can be applied usefully in any number of work situations.

Preparation and resources

You will need the Thinking skills for work CD, computer/s and/or an interactive white board.

Teaching points

You can allow students to form their own groups or you might prefer to place them in groups with an appropriate social and academic mix. The latter approach will, of course, need to be carried out sensitively.

You should use your discretion in allowing students to re-play the video clip. The number of times they do this will depend on the ability of the students.

You should ask each group to present their initial conclusions to the rest of the class in turn. Subsequent discussion should be carried out with the strict understanding that criticism and comment will be constructive and polite.

You should allow the students to carry out this exercise without explaining the transferable skills implicit in the aims. Unless individual students ask why they are doing an exercise like this you should leave any explanation until the end of the lesson.

Answers

Answers are not allowed under the code of conduct of the Magic Circle!

Menu, page 36

Aims

Students will:

- concentrate on oral information
- understand and analyse the information
- use the information to produce written instructions in an interesting format.

Preparation and resources

You will need the Thinking skills for work CD, computer/s and/or an interactive white board. Access to computer software to design the menu card and a kitchen if you do decide to allow students to prepare and cook the meal.

Teaching points

You should point out that this exercise is aimed at developing skills which are needed in many areas of employment – not just in catering. You should allow students to complete this exercise using appropriate computer software. The completed menu cards could be displayed and discussed as part of a plenary discussion. The dish is actually Spaghetti Carbonara. Some students might work this out but it would be interesting to see what other names are suggested. All discussion should be carried out in a constructive and supportive manner.

As an extension activity you could allow students to prepare and cook the meal described in the recipe. They could do this on their own or in small groups.

You can allow students to form their own groups or you might prefer to place them in groups with an appropriate social and academic mix. The latter approach will, of course, need to be carried out sensitively.

Following instructions – know your napkins, page 37

Aims

Students will:

- follow instructions given orally
- make the item described in the instructions (a folded napkin)
- evaluate the quality of the finished items
- consider the relative effectiveness of different ways of presenting and receiving information, for example, auditory and visual learning styles.

Teacher's notes and answers

Preparation and resources

You will need the Thinking skills for work CD, computer/s and/or an interactive white board. You will also need a napkin for each student. If this proves difficult, you can use a handkerchief or any suitable square of material.

Teaching points

You should point out that this exercise is aimed at developing skills which are needed in many areas of employment – not just in catering. You should ensure that when students go round looking at the finished napkins they do so in an orderly way and that any comments are made in a supportive and constructive way. However, this is intended to be a bit of fun. After students have looked at each other's napkins you should attempt to summarise the main opinions given in answers to questions 4, 5 and 6. This can be done as part of a whole-class discussion. If, as seems likely, the students state that the oral instructions were inadequate for their needs you should allow them a second attempt but with the help of the text and diagrams shown in the appendix on page 131.

Following instructions – serviette style, page 38

Aims

Students will:

- follow instructions which are presented in video format
- make the items described in the instructions (two folded napkins)
- evaluate the quality of the finished items
- consider the relative effectiveness of two different ways of presenting and receiving information
- produce guidelines for giving good instructions, based on their experiences.

Preparation and resources

You will need the Thinking skills for work CD, computer/s and/or an interactive white board. You will also need two napkins for each student. If this proves difficult, you can use a handkerchief or any suitable square of material.

Teaching points

You should point out that this exercise is aimed at developing skills which are needed in many areas of employment – not just in catering. You should ensure that when students go round looking at the finished napkins they do so in an orderly way and that any comments are made in a supportive and constructive way. However, this is intended to be a bit of fun.

You can allow students to form their own groups or you might prefer to place them in groups with an appropriate social and academic mix. The latter approach will, of course, need to be carried out sensitively. All members of the groups should have some input into the guidelines but they could be written out by one person acting as scribe. Each group can take turns to present their guidelines as part of a whole class discussion.

Darts, page 39

Aims

Students will:

- concentrate on a video clip of television sports commentary
- analyse the quality of the commentary with the help of a set of guidelines
- produce further guidelines
- write and present own commentary, working to the guidelines
- perform work to an audience, thus developing communication skills and self-confidence.

Preparation and resources

You will need the Thinking skills for work CD, computer/s and/or an interactive white board.

Teacher's notes and answers

Teaching points

Point out that this exercise is aimed at developing skills which are needed in many areas of employment. You could hold a whole-class discussion after students have watched the first video clip. For the second part of the lesson you could allow students to work in small groups. You can allow students to form their own groups or you might prefer to place them in groups with an appropriate social and academic mix. The latter approach will, of course, need to be carried out sensitively.

You could inform students that, as part of the training process, there will be a deadline for completion of the commentaries. Any discussion about the relative merits of the students' commentaries should be carried out in a supportive and constructive manner. You should not force students to perform if they are reluctant to do so.

Introducing Z Factor, pages 40–42

Aims

Students will:

- read and understand information presented as a web page
- answer factual questions relating to the information
- make inferences and deductions from the information
- ask questions aimed at eliciting further information.

Teaching points

Point out that this exercise is aimed at developing skills which are needed in many areas of employment. Students can read the web page to themselves or you can read it aloud to help less able students. Should anybody ask, Nestor Torres is a real person. He is a jazz flautist from Puerto Rico.

As a final activity students should form groups and role-play the radio station interview with the members of Z Factor. You can allow students to form their own groups or you might prefer to place them in groups with an appropriate social and academic mix. The latter approach will, of course, need to be carried out sensitively.

Answers

1. There are four people in the band.
2. The youngest member of the band is Angelica.
3. The oldest member of the band is Hovis.
4. The songwriters in the band are Dawson and Angelica.
5. Hovis Bean probably has a made-up name.
6. Percussion instruments are instruments that produce their sound by being struck or shaken, such as drums, tambourines, maracas and claves.
7. Flute, Saxophone, Clarinet
8. Knot Alone
9. £50,000
10. Z Factor would appear to be very popular because they have sold a lot of albums and also some of their tour dates are sold out.
11. There is no definitive answer to this question. However, the band would probably appeal to males and females in their late teens, possibly students or young professional people.
12. Questions should indicate that the information on the web page has been read and understood. They should also be interesting and designed to elicit further significant information about the band members, rather than asking about favourite food, fashions and television programmes.

Finish the lyrics, page 43

Aims

Students will:

- read unfinished song lyrics
- work collaboratively to analyse and discuss the meaning and structure of the song lyrics
- work collaboratively to complete song lyrics
- present work for discussion by the whole class.

Teaching points

Point out that this exercise is aimed at developing skills which are needed in many areas of employment. With less able students you might need to read the lyrics aloud to the class. Most students will benefit from an

Teacher's notes and answers

initial discussion about rhymes and rhythms as well as understanding the patterns in songs, including the ways in which verses and choruses are used to best effect.

If it proves difficult for all students to form suitable pairs you could allow them to work in groups of 3 or 4 but no more than this. You can allow students to form their own groups or you might prefer to place them in groups with an appropriate social and academic mix. The latter approach will, of course, need to be carried out sensitively.

As a final activity you should ask each pair or group to read out their lyrics and titles, focussing on one song at a time. These can be compared and discussed in a supportive and positive manner. Students could vote for their favourite set of lyrics for each song.

Breaking news, pages 44–46

Aims

Students will:

- read information presented in note form
- analyse that information
- present the information in a modified format for a different audience
- work as part of a group to meet a deadline
- consider and allocate the roles necessary for completion of the task
- rehearse and evaluate performance before completion
- cope with additional tasks introduced as they are working.

Preparation and resources

You will need copies of the breaking news items to hand out to students.

Teaching points

Point out that this exercise is aimed at developing skills which are needed in many areas of employment. You can allow students to form their own groups or you might prefer to place them in groups with an appropriate social and academic mix. The latter approach will, of course, need to be carried out sensitively.

With less able students you might need to read out the emails and discuss the content with them. You could allow them to write a script for a shorter bulletin of perhaps one minute. You should set a reasonable deadline for completion of the scripts. The breaking news items should be copied prior to the lesson and cut up into separate items. These can be introduced at intervals and given to the director of each group while the students are working. With less able students you can read them out as well as giving them to the director.

You should give regular time checks and approximately one minute before the deadline all work should stop. After a ten second countdown each group should present their news programme in turn. The running order should not be revealed before this point. You should allow a gap of no more than one minute between each group.

If groups finish before the allocated time, this should be noted. If they are still talking at the end of the allocated time they should be cut off.

When all the groups have read you should hold a plenary discussion in which performances are assessed. This should be carried out in a constructive and supportive manner.

News headlines, page 47

Aims

Students will:

- listen to oral information
- analyse that information
- present the information in a modified format for a different audience
- work as part of a group to meet a deadline
- consider and allocate the roles necessary for completion of the task
- rehearse and evaluate performance before completion.

Preparation and resources

You will need the Thinking skills for work CD, computer/s and/or an interactive white board.

Teacher's notes and answers

Teaching points

Point out that this exercise is aimed at developing skills which are needed in many areas of employment. You can allow students to form their own groups or you might prefer to place them in groups with an appropriate social and academic mix. The latter approach will, of course, need to be carried out sensitively. No work should be permitted after the 30-minute deadline. Groups should be encouraged to perform their work in turn to the rest of the class. The performances should be discussed and evaluated in a supportive manner.

As an extension activity the class could draw up a list of 'Hints for newsreaders'.

Picture this, pages 48–49

Aims

Students will:

- concentrate on visual information in the form of a picture
- memorise, recall and reproduce the picture when they can no longer see it
- analyse ability to memorise, recall and reproduce visual information
- compare own abilities in these areas with those of others.

Preparation and resources

You will need to give each student a copy of pictures 1 and 2 and sheets of blank paper.

Teaching points

The pictures for this activity are on one sheet. It is recommended that you fold the page in half or cover the first or second picture so that students are only able to see either picture 1 or picture 2, depending on which questions they are doing.

It is important to carry out this exercise according to the following instructions.

Give each student a copy of the worksheet showing pictures 1 and 2. The picture should be laid face down in front of them. When everyone has a copy of the picture, instruct students to turn over the sheet.

Allow exactly one minute for them to look at picture 1. After one minute, tell all students to turn the sheet over, face down. Collect the sheets and give out copies of the activity sheet. Students should answer questions 1–4.

Now carry out the same instructions for picture 2. Once students have looked at the picture for one minute, tell all the students to turn the sheet over, face down. Collect the sheets and ask students to answer questions 5–8.

Students who are not good artists can draw sketches using stick figures for people if they wish. Give out copies of picture 1 and picture 2, allowing students to assess their work. This should be followed by a whole-class discussion during which results and opinions can be compared.

Picture that, pages 50–51

Aims

Students will:

- concentrate on visual information in the form of a picture
- memorise and recall the picture when they can no longer see it
- communicate the details remembered from the picture, in speech, to another person to enable that person to reproduce the picture
- listen to details of a picture memorised by another person and attempt to draw the picture from those details
- analyse ability to memorise, recall, communicate and reproduce visual information
- compare own abilities in these areas with those of others.

Preparation and resources

You will need to give each student either a copy of picture 1 or picture 2, along with pieces of drawing paper.

Teaching points

Point out that this exercise is aimed at developing skills which are needed in many areas of employment.

Teacher's notes and answers

It is important to carry out this exercise according to the following instructions.

Ask students to work in pairs. You can allow them to form their own pairs or you might prefer to place each person with a suitable partner. The latter approach will, of course, need to be carried out sensitively. Tell each person to sit away from their partner. Give one person in each pair a copy of picture 1. Give the other person a copy of picture 2. These should be laid face down in front of them. When everyone has a copy of a picture, instruct students to turn over the sheet. Allow exactly one minute for them to look at it. After one minute, tell all students to fold the sheet over or cover the picture, so only the questions are in view and hand out blank pieces of paper. Students should carry out questions 1 and 2. You will need to allow a suitable amount of time for completion of these questions. At the end of the set time, tell students to stop. You can then tell students to look at the original pictures at the top of the worksheets, allowing students to assess their work. Ask the students to complete question 3. This should be followed by a whole-class discussion during which results and opinions can be compared.

As an extension activity, ask students to begin to formulate a set of guidelines for improving skills in the areas of memory, recall and communication of visual information.

Picture these, pages 52–54

Aims

Students will:

- concentrate on visual information in the form of a diagram
- memorise and recall the diagram when they can no longer see it
- draw a labelled diagram of their own
- submit their work for supportive criticism, as part of a whole-class analysis of the ability to memorise, recall, communicate and reproduce visual information.

Preparation and resources

You will need to give each student copies of diagrams 1 and 2, the worksheet on page 53 and blank sheets of paper.

Teaching points

Point out that this exercise is aimed at developing skills which are needed in many areas of employment.

It is important to carry out this exercise according to the following instructions.

Give each student a copy of the sheets showing diagrams 1 and 2. This should be laid face down in front of them. When everyone has a copy of the sheet, instruct students to fold the sheet in half or cover diagram 2 and turn over the sheet. Allow exactly one minute for them to look at diagram 1. After one minute, tell all students to turn the sheet over, face down. Collect the sheets, give out copies of the next worksheet and ask students to answer question 3. Again, you may need to ask students to cover up question 4 or fold the worksheet in half.

Give each student a copy of the sheets showing diagrams 1 and 2. This should be laid face down in front of them. When everyone has a copy of the sheet, instruct students to fold the sheet in half or cover diagram 1 and turn over the sheet. Allow exactly one minute for them to look at it. After one minute, tell all students to turn the sheet over, face down. Collect the sheets, give out copies of the next worksheet and ask students to answer question 4. Again, you may need to ask students to cover up question 3 or fold the worksheet in half.

Once students have completed the activities, give out copies of diagrams 1 and 2 again and allow students time to check the accuracy of their labelling. Then give out the final worksheet and a piece of drawing paper. Go through the guidelines and ask students to complete question 5.

Display the finished work and allow students to look at it. This should be followed by a whole-class discussion during which results and opinions can be compared.

Students should finalise their guidelines for improving skills in the areas of memory, recall and communication of visual information.

Teacher's notes and answers

The Daily Blag, pages 55–56

Aims

Students will:

- understand and follow written instructions
- complete unfinished text using clues and guidelines
- create a narrative text based on a headline and related words and numbers
- work cooperatively to assess the quality of work produced by members of the class.

Teaching points

Point out that this exercise is aimed at developing skills which are needed in many areas of employment.

Less able students could be allowed to work in pairs or small groups. You can allow students to form their own pairs and groups or you might prefer to place them in groups with an appropriate social and academic mix. The latter approach will, of course, need to be carried out sensitively.

In the second part of the lesson, the number of articles the students write will depend on their abilities and the time available. Less able students could be allowed to choose one rather than attempt to complete all three.

Students can read out their finished articles as part of a constructive, whole-class discussion focussing on the effectiveness of writing styles. Written work should also be assessed for spelling and punctuation.

Answers

Dog Saves Hamster's Life

Rupert the Rotweiler didn't *panic* when his little *pal*, Harry the *Hamster*, fell into the fish *pond*. Rupert ran to his *owner*, seven-year-old Dylan Donlan, and raised the *alarm*.

"He barked and barked," said Dylan, "and then he *grabbed* my arm in his mouth and pulled me into the *garden*."

By the time Dylan's dad, Dennis, arrived to *help*, Harry was back on *dry* land.

"He couldn't get out of the pond and a *big* fish was after him. Rupert *scared* off the fish and I pulled Harry out," said Dylan.

Dennis has *filled* in the pond at his home in Halifax, and *entered* Rupert for the annual 'Pet Hero' award. Harry seems to have *suffered* no lasting damage and yesterday he was playing *happily* in the garden with Rupert and Dylan.

Interest Rates Set to Rise

The Bank of *England* is expected to *increase* interest rates to *4.5%* tomorrow. Financial experts predict that the current *economic* climate has made an increase inevitable. This will affect *inflation* and increase the burden on house-buyers. *Mortgage* providers are expected to increase their rates by at least 0.5%. The Prime Minister made a *statement* in Parliament.

Pedalo power, pages 57–58

Aims

Students will:

- concentrate on spoken information in the form of a radio news item
- recall the information and use it in different formats
- work with others to extend the radio news item using questions and answers of their own
- perform work to an audience, thus developing communication skills and self-confidence.

Preparation and resources

You will need the Thinking skills for work CD, computer/s and/or an interactive white board.

Teaching points

Point out that this exercise is aimed at developing skills which are needed in many areas of employment.

You should use your discretion as to whether students should be allowed to listen to the audio clip for a second time before answering the first set of questions.

You can allow students to form their own groups or you might prefer to place them in groups with an appropriate social and academic mix. The latter approach will, of course, need to be carried out sensitively.

Teacher's notes and answers

In question 2, less able students might need help with separating facts from opinions about Brian. For question 4, less able students could just write an introductory paragraph to the story for *The Daily World*, while more able students could write a full article. All members of the groups should have some input into the questions for the press conference but you should allow them to play to their strengths. They could be allowed the option of choosing one or more people to act as scribes. You should point out that this exercise is intended to be a bit of fun and suggest that questions and answers can be humorous within the context that has been established.

You might need to explain the purpose of a press conference and the way in which a press conference is organised. This should lead on to a discussion of the possible characters in the role-play, for example: the manager of The Slug and Cabbage, Brian, Tina, Tyler, Tom, a representative of *The Daily World*, various reporters, friends of the Chuffs. You should set a time limit on preparation and give a deadline for performing the press conferences. Students who do not feel comfortable performing should not be forced to do so. The role-plays can be performed in turn to the whole class and assessed in a constructive and supportive manner.

Answers

1. The fact-file should include the fact that Brian:
   - is 32 years old
   - lives in Yorkshire
   - has a wife named Tina and two children named Tyler and Tom, both aged 12
   - drinks in The Slug and Cabbage.
2. Opinions should refer to the points suggested but students should be encouraged to form more of their own, as long as they can point to evidence in the story.
3. Brian was offered money by *The Daily World* because the sponsorship is probably related to the connection between what Brian is doing and the name of the paper. It will also be an interesting story that will sell papers and it will associate the paper with a popular achievement.

The fishing line, page 59

Aims

Students will:

- concentrate on information presented orally in the form of an audio clip of a radio sports programme
- recall the information
- take part in a critical discussion about the programme in the video clip
- present criticisms in the form of an email to a person in authority
- write and present a follow-up programme of their own, working to guidelines
- perform work to an audience, thus developing communication skills and self-confidence.

Preparation and resources

You will need the Thinking skills for work CD, computer/s and/or an interactive white board and access to email software.

Teaching points

Point out that this exercise is aimed at developing skills which are needed in many areas of employment.

You should use your discretion as to whether students should be allowed to listen to the audio clip for a second time before answering the first set of questions.

You could discuss question 3 before asking students to answer it. They should consider the opinions of people other than themselves.

You could hold a whole-class discussion before asking students to work on the second set of questions. You will have to be sensitive to the feelings of any students whose hobby is fishing. You can allow students to form their own groups or you might prefer to place them in groups with an appropriate social and academic mix. The latter approach will, of course, need to be carried out sensitively. Allow students to write their answer to question 4 using email software if you have access to it.

Teacher's notes and answers

Each group could take turns to present their answers and act out their interviews as part of a whole-class discussion. The discussion should be carried out in a supportive and constructive manner. You should not force students to perform if they are reluctant to do so.

Answers

1. a) Radio Ripley
   b) John Pike
   c) The Fishing Line
2. a) Eric Hopley was dangling his float.
   b) Amy Johnson was looking for her lost maggot.
   c) Frank Bodger was doing nothing.
   d) Hugh Williams was reeling in an old bike.
3. Answers should reflect students' own opinions and many of them might think this a boring event/programme but they should also consider the likely opinions of other people, some of whom might agree with the presenter.

Public speaking, pages 60–61

Aims

Students will:

- concentrate on a video clip of different people making speeches
- produce a critical analysis of the performances on the video clip
- discuss, compare and justify opinions as part of a whole-class activity
- work with the whole group to draw up guidelines for improving speech-making.

Preparation and resources

You will need the Thinking skills for work CD, computer/s and/or an interactive white board.

Teaching points

Point out that this exercise is aimed at developing skills which are needed in many areas of employment.

To help students to judge how good each speech was use the Guidelines for writing a speech and Guidelines for giving a speech in the appendix on page 132.

You should allow students to repeat the video clips if they wish to do so.

You will need to discuss the best ways to compare the opinions and scores within the whole class. You could work out average scores, or simply ask each person which speech they thought was best and which they thought was worst and then add up the totals for each. You should also ask for volunteers to read out their opinions. All discussion should be carried out in a supportive and constructive manner.

Speaking in public, pages 62–65

Aims

Students will:

- analyse situations involving speaking to people
- practise and perform role-plays about speaking to people
- discuss and analyse performances
- work with others to develop strategies to help them cope in situations where they have to speak to people as part of their job.

Teaching points

Point out that this exercise is aimed at developing skills which are needed in many areas of employment.

With less able students you might need to read the four stories aloud.

To help students to judge how good each speech was use the Guidelines for writing a speech and Guidelines for giving a speech in the appendix on page 132.

You can allow students to form their own groups or you could place them in groups with an appropriate social and academic mix. The latter approach will have to be carried out sensitively. More able students could learn their 'speeches' by heart and present them without reading from a script. You could ask each group in turn to read out their suggested guidelines and use these as a basis for a plenary discussion. All discussion should be carried out in a supportive and constructive manner.

Teacher's notes and answers

Answers

1. Ultimately, it might have helped Fatima to improve her confidence but at the time asking her to introduce herself in front of the whole office caused her distress.
2. Fatima was embarrassed by what her boss said. She went red and her mind went blank.
4. A role-play involves people playing a part as in a play. The aim of a role-play is to develop empathy for others and to illustrate situations.
5. Tom might have hated role-plays because he was shy.
6. Ultimately, it might have helped Tom to improve his confidence but at the time it caused him some distress and it wasn't very fair of the lecturer.
8. Sarah was probably terrified when the manager left her in charge because she had never had this much responsibility before and didn't know what to expect.
9. Ultimately, it might have helped Sarah to improve her confidence but at the time being left in charge caused her some distress.
11. Patrick probably said: "I'm only on work experience" to give himself an excuse not to answer the man.
12. It wasn't a good thing to say because you are supposed to show initiative on work experience.

Listen carefully, page 66

Aims

Students will:

- concentrate on a set of oral instructions
- remember and follow the instructions
- assess performances in following the instructions
- draw up guidelines aimed at improving concentration and memory
- test those guidelines
- discuss their effectiveness
- consider the application of these skills in everyday work situations.

Preparation and resources

You will need the Thinking skills for work CD, computer/s and/or an interactive white board.

Teaching points

Point out that this exercise is aimed at developing skills which are needed in many areas of employment.

This lesson is intended to be fun but you should remind students of the need for common sense. All discussion should be carried out in a supportive and constructive manner. Students might need help in thinking about how the skills learnt in this lesson can be transferred to other situations. You could point out the fact that, in work, most instructions are given verbally and that there is often no time to repeat them.

Customer care 1, pages 67–68

Aims

Students will:

- concentrate and remember information
- recall and present information in a logical context
- analyse events
- propose alternative courses of action in a work situation
- relate to and learn from observations of social interactions.

Preparation and resources

You will need the Thinking skills for work CD, computer/s and/or an interactive white board.

Teaching points

Point out that this exercise is aimed at developing skills which are needed in many areas of employment.

The first set of questions is more straightforward than the second. Depending on the ability of your group you can ask students to tackle them all at once or get them to answer the first set, review their answers and then go on to the next. You can use the questions as the basis for a discussion about the need for concentration and ways in which people can improve their abilities to remember facts.

Teacher's notes and answers

You can allow students to form their own groups or you might prefer to place them in groups with an appropriate social and academic mix. The latter approach will, of course, need to be carried out sensitively.

You should use your discretion in allowing students to re-play the video clip. The number of times they do this will depend on the ability of the students.

Answers

1. The woman bought a sports top back to the store.
2. The top cost the woman £95.
3. The woman bought the item two weeks ago.
4. The assistant asked for a receipt.
5. The woman said the item had shrunk.
6. The assistant said the top was meant to be tight-fitting.
7. The top was a size 12.
8. The assistant wanted to look at the label to check that she had followed the washing instructions.
9. The woman's tumble-dryer was a Bosch.
10. The woman wanted the assistant to refund her money.
11. First the assistant offered to exchange the item. Later he offered to refund her money – if she had the receipt.
12. The assistant was going to say that she originally said that she had bought the item but then changed her story, saying it had been a gift.

There are no definitive answers to the second group of questions. Students should be expected to give opinions which show that they have considered and discussed the issues and come up with reasonable opinions and conclusions.

Customer care 2, pages 69–70

Aims

Students will:

- concentrate and remember information
- recall and present information in a logical context
- analyse events
- propose alternative courses of action in a work situation
- relate to and learn from observations of social interaction.

Preparation and resources

You will need the Thinking skills for work CD, computer/s and/or an interactive white board.

Teaching points

Point out that this exercise is aimed at developing skills which are needed in many areas of employment.

The first set of questions is more straightforward than the second. Depending on the ability of your group you can ask students to tackle them all at once or get them to answer the first set, review their answers and then go on to the next. You can use the questions as the basis for a discussion about the need for concentration and ways in which people can improve their abilities to remember facts.

You can allow students to form their own groups or you might prefer to place them in groups with an appropriate social and academic mix. The latter approach will, of course, need to be carried out sensitively.

You should use your discretion in allowing students to re-play the video clip. The number of times they do this will depend on the ability of the students.

Answers

1. The name of the garage was Terry's Garage.
2. When the woman came in, the mechanic was texting on his phone.
3. The woman thought the tyre had a slow puncture.
4. The woman's car was a Nissan.
5. The woman had owned the car for two years.
6. The mechanic thought the Audi was her car.
7. The mechanic spoke to someone called Robbie on the phone.
8. The woman asked the mechanic to look at the tyre on the back right.
9. The mechanic took about ten seconds to look at the tyres.

Teacher's notes and answers

10. The mechanic said there was a gash in the side wall of the tyre.
11. The mechanic said the other tyres were all worn and had treads on the legal limit of 1.6 mm.
12. He offered to fit PX95s.
13. It would cost £192 to get all four tyres fitted.
14. The mechanic told the woman to call back at 11.45 for her car.

There are no definitive answers to the second group of questions. Students should be expected to give opinions which show that they have considered and discussed the issues and come up with reasonable opinions and conclusions.

Customer care 3, pages 71–72

Aims

Students will:

- read and understand a formal letter
- extract the important pieces of information from that letter
- formulate a response to complaints made in the letter
- write a letter outlining a proposed response.

Teaching points

Point out that this exercise is aimed at developing skills which are needed in many areas of employment.

Less able students may need help reading the letter. You could allow them to work in pairs or small groups. You can allow students to form their own groups or you might prefer to place them in groups with an appropriate social and academic mix. The latter approach will, of course, need to be carried out sensitively.

If your students have had little or no experience of staying in hotels you might need to discuss the procedures involved. You could also point out that most of them will, at some stage, stay in a hotel, either for work or pleasure, and that some of them might even work in a hotel.

You could carry out the following extension activities:

- students take turns to read and discuss their letters
- students work in groups to devise a role-play in which the hotel manager speaks to Eric and Katrina about the letter of complaint. The role-plays could be performed and discussed.

Phone calls, page 73

Aims

Students will:

- concentrate on situations recorded in an audio clip
- remember relevant information from the audio clip
- make critical observations about the situations in the audio clip
- respond to a simulated phone conversation
- perform these simulations to an audience
- work as part of a group to draw up guidelines for defusing difficult situations at work when dealing with people on the phone.

Preparation and resources

You will need the Thinking skills for work CD, computer/s and/or an interactive white board.

Teaching points

Point out that this exercise is aimed at developing skills which are needed in many areas of employment.

You should use your discretion as to whether students should be allowed to listen to the audio clips for a second time before answering the questions. You can allow students to form their own groups or you might prefer to place them in groups with an appropriate social and academic mix. The latter approach will, of course, need to be carried out sensitively. All discussions should take place in a constructive and supportive manner.

Teacher's notes and answers

Answers

1. The man was phoning the city council because his bin had not been emptied for four weeks.
2. The man's postcode was DB14 6NY.
3. Sarah-Jane said the man's bins were due to be emptied on Thursdays.
4. Bank Holidays are on Mondays and the work that would normally be done on Monday would be done later in the week, which would affect collections on the other days of that week.
5. Bins have to be placed outside the property in order for them to be emptied:
    - in case of any accidents/incidents on the resident's property which could be blamed on the bin men
    - to cut down the time spent in collecting, emptying and returning the bins.

Satisfied customers, pages 74–76

Aims

Students will:

- read, understand and analyse information relating to customer service
- relate that information to own experiences
- work with others to predict the likely effects of good customer service
- work with others to draw up guidelines for providing good customer service.

Teaching points

Point out that this exercise is aimed at developing skills which are needed in many areas of employment.

You can allow students to form their own groups or you might prefer to place them in groups with an appropriate social and academic mix. The latter approach will, of course, need to be carried out sensitively. Depending on the abilities of your students you might need to help them in some of their discussions. Some answers will depend on students' opinions but they should be logical and show an understanding of the issues.

Answers

1. John Lewis gave the best customer service.
2. Local Councils gave the worst customer service.

6. 'Be helpful even if there's no immediate profit in it' means be helpful in any way that will please the customer, not just in ways that will make you money. This will benefit the company financially in the long term. For example, if your staff open doors for customers it won't make money but it might make customers want to come back.
7. Take the extra step: If a customer asks, "Where are the biscuits?" don't just tell them, go with them and show them, then ask if they need anything else.

    Throw in something extra: Give customers a discount coupon for next time they come in, offer to wrap a gift, give a smile.
8. It has been shown that good customer service:
    - can increase profits by 24%
    - can make it twice as likely that staff will stay with a company
    - can make it three times more likely that customers will recommend the products, services or company.

Help!, pages 77–78

Aims

Students will:

- listen to, analyse and make judgements about information in an audio clip
- suggest appropriate responses to situations portrayed in the audio clip
- compare and discuss alternative responses with others
- plan and take part in a short role-play based on those responses.

Preparation and resources

You will need the Thinking skills for work CD, computer/s and/or an interactive white board.

Teacher's notes and answers

Teaching points

Point out that this exercise is aimed at developing skills which are needed in many areas of employment.

You can allow students to form their own groups or you might prefer to place them in groups with an appropriate social and academic mix. The latter approach will, of course, need to be carried out sensitively.

All students should be encouraged to take part in the role-play. You should explain that this will help to increase self-confidence. However, those who are not comfortable in doing so should be allowed to present their work in written form – as a script or an account. It should be clearly understood that performances should be received in a respectful manner. The role-plays could be discussed constructively as part of a final plenary session. You should ensure that as part of this exercise students understand the serious consequences of so-called 'hoax' 999 calls.

Answers

8 and 9. When operators receive silent calls they ask the caller to tap the handset screen if they cannot speak. If this is done, or there are suspicious sounds in the background, the call is connected to the police.

16. Emergency call operators should speak clearly, keep calm and reassure the caller, ask questions that will help the emergency services to deal with the situation, such as where the person is phoning from and what exactly has happened, provide any helpful advice that you have been trained to give.

17. Callers should speak slowly and clearly, giving only important and relevant information, including their name and location. They should listen to any advice given by the operator and try to stay calm.

The boss blunders, pages 79–80

Aims

Students will:

- read and make corrections to a piece of illustrated text in the form of a flyer
- analyse the purpose of a flyer
- analyse the factors which make a flyer effective
- make appropriate suggestions to a senior colleague who has produced a piece of work that is unfit for purpose
- design an alternative, improved version of the flyer
- assess designs made by others.

Preparation and resources

If possible it would be good to have access to computers to design the flyers.

Teaching points

Point out that this exercise is aimed at developing skills which are needed in many areas of employment.

With less able students you could cover some or all of the questions in a whole-class discussion. Students could work in pairs or small groups to answer questions 6 and 7. You can allow students to form their own groups and pairs or you might prefer to place them in groups with an appropriate social and academic mix. The latter approach will, of course, need to be carried out sensitively.

Discussion of the finished flyer designs should be carried out in a positive and supportive manner. If there is no clear consensus, you could ask students to vote for the designs they find most effective. Less able students will need help in counting the votes.

Answers

1. Flyers are a relatively cheap form of advertising which can be distributed quickly, either door to door or by handing them out to passers-by.
2. An effective flyer contains clear and accurate information relating to the service or product it is advertising. It should be presented in an eye-catching way.

Teacher's notes and answers

3. and 4.

Mistakes	*Corrections*	*Mistakes*	*Corrections*
Telefone	*Telephone*	*pizza's*	*pizzas*
Febuary	*February*	*ingreedient's*	*ingredients*
mangement	*management*	*weak*	*week*
dailey	*daily*	*piza*	*pizza*
midnite	*midnight*	*drunk*	*drink*
delivry	*delivery*	*galric*	*garlic*
checks	*cheques*	*cusuine*	*cuisine*
excepted	*accepted*	*Authetnic*	*Authentic*

A phone call from the boss, pages 81–82

Aims

Students will:

- concentrate on verbal instructions
- make notes
- use initiative in dealing with problems
- prioritise and apply time management techniques
- work with others to discuss and resolve problems
- evaluate own performance and those of others.

Preparation and resources

You will need the Thinking skills for work CD, computer/s and/or an interactive white board.

Teaching points

Point out that this exercise is aimed at developing skills which are needed in many areas of employment.

The first set of questions is more straightforward than the second. You can use the questions as the basis for a discussion about the need for concentration and ways in which people can improve their abilities to remember facts. You should use your discretion in giving students a second chance by re-playing the audio clip.

You can allow students to form their own groups or you might prefer to place them in groups with an appropriate social and academic mix. The latter approach will, of course, need to be carried out sensitively.

You should tell students to work on the assumption that they have received the phone call in the office in which they usually work but that the call has come through to them because no one else was available.

Answers

1. The name of the person making the call was Jo.
2. Jo was calling from Madrid Airport.
3. Her new flight number was BA 8127.
4. The plane was due to land at Manchester Airport, probably at Terminal 3.
5. The plane was due to arrive at 13.42.
6. Jo was due to meet Barbara at 13.00.
7. The meeting was at the Hilton Hotel, Birmingham.
8. They were supposed to be meeting the clients at 13.30.
9. Jo asked you to pass on the following information to Barbara:
    - that her flight had been delayed
    - the new time of arrival
    - to start without her
    - that the name of the clients' boss was Geoff Samuels
    - to contact Andy to get information via email.

Answers to the second set of questions are much more open-ended but you could introduce the following points:

- How could you check whether the flight does, in fact, arrive at Terminal 3?
- How would you make sure the taxi firm you contact is reliable?
- How many Hilton Hotels are there in Birmingham?
- How can you contact Barbara and anyone else you might need to speak to?

Teacher's notes and answers

You should not put students under any undue pressure to perform as part of their response to question 19 but you should encourage students who are confident in this area. Answers to question 16 and question 19 could be used as a basis for a plenary discussion.

When things go wrong, pages 83–85

Aims

Students will:

- concentrate on written and verbal information
- use initiative in dealing with problems
- prioritise and apply time management techniques
- work with others to discuss and resolve problems
- adapt responses in accordance with changing circumstances
- evaluate own performances and those of others.

Teaching points

Point out that this exercise is aimed at developing skills which are needed in many areas of employment.

For the first section based at the restaurant, less able students could be allowed to work with a partner. You can allow students to form their own pairs or you might prefer to place them in pairs with an appropriate social and academic mix. The latter approach will, of course, need to be carried out sensitively. You could begin with a whole-class discussion using one job as an example. As far as possible, you should encourage second-phase thinking. For example, if the heating is found to be faulty, deciding how it could be repaired, perhaps by contacting a maintenance company. Students' answers could be compared and discussed in a positive and supportive manner. In particular, it would be useful to see to what extent students agreed about the order in which the jobs should be prioritised.

Problems for the surprise party

You should read these out at intervals of between 1 and 4 minutes, depending on the abilities of students.

1. At 12.30 pm you receive a phone call from the events manager at the hotel saying that the room you wanted has been double-booked and asking if you would mind changing to a room half the size that would cost less.
2. At 1.45 pm the operations manager phones to remind you that his wife is a vegetarian and doesn't eat meat or fish.
3. At 3.30 pm a junior colleague tells you that he is not going to wear a suit and that he will be wearing jeans, trainers and a 'heavy metal' t-shirt.
4. At 4.15 pm you receive a phone call from a key manager saying that she has had a disaster at the hairdressers and will have to do her hair again. She was supposed to meet the boss at her house at 7 pm and says she won't be there on time.
5. At 5.35 pm the Australian director phones to say that his flight has been delayed and he has only just landed. He has missed the train he was going to catch and it will take him at least an hour to get to your house even if he gets a taxi.
6. At 6.05 pm the DJ phones to say that he had asked you to let him know if you have any special requests for the type of music you want him to play.
7. At 6.30 pm you can't find the tickets for the surprise holiday.
8. At 6.35 pm the limo driver phones to say he is two miles away and has had a puncture.
9. At 6.40 pm two close colleagues of your boss call you to say they are going round to the boss's house with a present and you realise that you have not invited them to the party.
10. At 6.45 pm you arrive at your boss's house and she is not ready because she doesn't think there is any need to rush.

Less able students could be allowed to work with a partner. You can allow students to form their own pairs or you might prefer to place them in pairs with an

Teacher's notes and answers

appropriate social and academic mix. The latter approach will, of course, need to be carried out sensitively.

You could begin with a whole-class discussion using one of the problems as an example. Again, as far as possible, you should encourage second-phase thinking.

Students' answers could be compared and discussed in a positive and supportive manner.

Eyewitness, pages 86–88

Aims

Students will:

- concentrate on and remember visual information
- recall and present that information in a logical context, orally and in writing
- analyse events and actions
- suggest ways of improving observational skills.

Preparation and resources

You will need the Thinking skills for work CD, computer/s and/or an interactive white board.

Teaching points

Students can work alone or in small groups. You can allow students to form their own groups or you might prefer to place them in groups with an appropriate social and academic mix. The latter approach will, of course, need to be carried out sensitively. You can use the students' answers in a whole-class discussion.

Every picture tells a story, page 89

Aims

Students will:

- interpret body language as seen in still photographs
- compare interpretations with those of others
- analyse the 'clues' to interpretation which are given in body language
- discuss the degree to which different interpretations of the events portrayed in the photographs can be made
- apply this learning to different contexts.

Preparation and resources

You will need the Thinking skills for work CD, computer/s and/or an interactive white board.

Teaching points

Point out that this exercise is aimed at developing skills which are needed in many areas of employment.

You can allow students to form their own groups or you might prefer to place them in groups with an appropriate social and academic mix. The latter approach will, of course, need to be carried out sensitively.

Depending on the abilities of your students you might need to help them in their discussions about how the body language in the pictures can be interpreted.

You could suggest to students that when they are working in their groups they could agree upon a suitable caption for each of the pictures.

As part of the final discussion you should ask students to consider the relevance of this exercise to everyday life. If they find it difficult to do so you could talk about:

- the ways in which we make assumptions about people after only seeing them for a few seconds and the effects of those assumptions on social and working relationships
- the impressions we give to others about ourselves through our body language and non-verbal behaviour
- the fact that we are very quick to make assumptions based on body language
- the degree to which we can change initial assumptions based on interpretations of body language.

All members of the groups should have some input into the discussion but the main points could be written by one person acting as scribe. Question 5 can be answered as part of a whole-class discussion, as part of a group discussion or by students on their own. The whole-class discussions should be carried out in a constructive and supportive manner.

Teacher's notes and answers

Body language 1, pages 90–93

Aims

Students will:

- interpret body language as seen in still photographs
- compare own interpretations with those of others
- analyse the 'clues' to interpretation which are given in the body language
- discuss the degree to which different interpretations of the events portrayed in the photographs can be made
- apply this learning to social and work contexts
- understand the importance of body language in perception of others.

Preparation and resources

You will need the Thinking skills for work CD, computer/s and/or an interactive white board.

Teaching points

Point out that this exercise is aimed at developing skills which are needed in many areas of employment.

You can allow students to form their own groups or you might prefer to place them in groups with an appropriate social and academic mix. The latter approach will, of course, need to be carried out sensitively.

Depending on the abilities of your students you might need to help them in their discussions about how the body language in the pictures can be interpreted. The body language of the person in clip 2a could be analysed as part of a whole-class discussion.

Question 22 could be answered by a show of hands. Depending on the ability of the students you might need to help with the counting.

If some of the questions appear to cover similar ground this is intentional and designed to make students consider different perspectives, such as work and social situations.

As part of the final discussion you should ask students to consider the relevance of this exercise to everyday life. If they find it difficult to do so you could talk about:

- the ways in which we make assumptions about people after only seeing them for a few seconds and the effects of those assumptions on social and working relationships
- the impressions we give to others about ourselves through our body language and non-verbal behaviour
- the fact that we are very quick to make assumptions based on body language
- the degree to which we can change initial assumptions based on interpretations of our body language.

The whole-class discussions should be carried out in a constructive and supportive manner.

Body language 2, pages 94–97

Aims

Students will:

- interpret body language as seen in video clips
- compare own interpretations with those of others
- analyse the 'clues' to interpretation which are given in the body language
- discuss the degree to which different interpretations of the events portrayed in the video clips can be made
- apply this learning to social and work contexts
- explore the effects of body language on others
- understand the differences between appropriate and inappropriate body language.

Preparation and resources

You will need the Thinking skills for work CD, computer/s and/or an interactive white board.

Teacher's notes and answers

Teaching points

Point out that this exercise is aimed at developing skills which are needed in many areas of employment.

You can allow students to form their own groups or you might prefer to place them in groups with an appropriate social and academic mix. The latter approach will, of course, need to be carried out sensitively.

Depending on the abilities of your students you might need to help them in their discussions about how the body language can be interpreted. The body language of the person in clip 11a could be analysed as part of a whole-class discussion.

You should discuss the concept of 'self-image' to ensure that students understand it.

Question 26 could be answered by a show of hands. Depending on the ability of the students you might need to help with the counting.

You will need to explain that the terms 'best' and 'worst' body language refer to the degree to which the body language is appropriate or inappropriate and whether it is likely to have a positive or negative impact on others.

If some of the questions appear to cover similar ground this is intentional and designed to make students consider different perspectives, such as work and social situations.

As part of the final discussion you should ask students to consider the relevance of this exercise to everyday life. If they find it difficult to do so you could talk about:

- the ways in which we make assumptions about people after only seeing them for a few seconds and the effects of those assumptions on social and working relationships
- the impressions we give to others about ourselves through our body language and non-verbal behaviour
- the fact that we are very quick to make assumptions based on body language
- the degree to which we can change initial assumptions based on interpretations of our body language.

The whole-class discussions should be carried out in a constructive and supportive manner. As an extension activity, students could work in groups to devise a role-play based on the situations in the video clip.

Stranded, pages 98–100

Aims

Students will:

- read a map
- read text describing a situation relating to the map
- work in a group, using the map and instructions to agree upon responses to a number of specified situations
- use imagination to write a short story based on the tasks.

Teaching points

Point out that this exercise is aimed at developing skills which are needed in many areas of employment.

You can allow students to form their own groups or you might prefer to place them in groups with an appropriate social and academic mix. The latter approach will, of course, need to be carried out sensitively. Depending on the abilities of your students you might need to help them in some of their discussions.

You could hold a whole-class discussion in which groups share their answers and stories. They should be encouraged to talk about the issues they encountered in attempting to find joint solutions to the questions and problems presented to them. This could stimulate a further discussion on the dynamics of group interaction.

Answers

There are no definitive answers but students should show logic and understanding in their responses.

Teacher's notes and answers

Assessment and evaluation, page 101

Aims

Students will:

- self-assess work on Thinking Skills for Work.

Preparation and resources

It would be helpful for students to have the work they have done on this book to hand when they carry out this activity. You might need to spend some time briefly going over the work they have covered.
You should also allow time for students to go through any relevant coursework or notes. You will also need to give out the checklist on pages 102–103 or project it on a whiteboard.

Teaching points

Less able students might find it difficult to complete this exercise. You should explain the importance of assessment and evaluation and spend some time discussing the questions as a class before asking students to complete their answers. Begin by explaining the purpose of the exercise; namely that it is designed to help students assess their progress and also to provide information that will help the course tutor to evaluate the course. It could also provide valuable feedback that could be incorporated into future teaching of this topic. Encourage students to be honest and realistic. They should not assess themselves too highly but neither should they be too critical of themselves.

Stress the fact that the information in the assessment is confidential and will not be shared with others in the class. However, some students might prefer to hand in their assessment anonymously and you could allow them to do so.

Appendix 1

Here are the visuals for Following instructions – know your napkins, page 37.

1. Place the napkin facedown in front of you.

2. Fold the napkin in half diagonally.

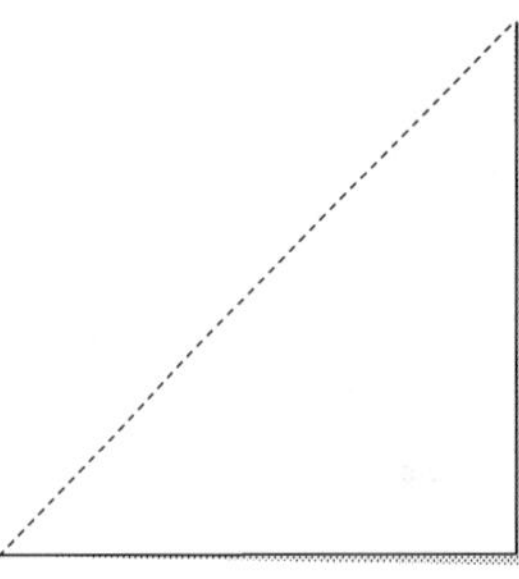

3. Place the napkin with the long side on the left.

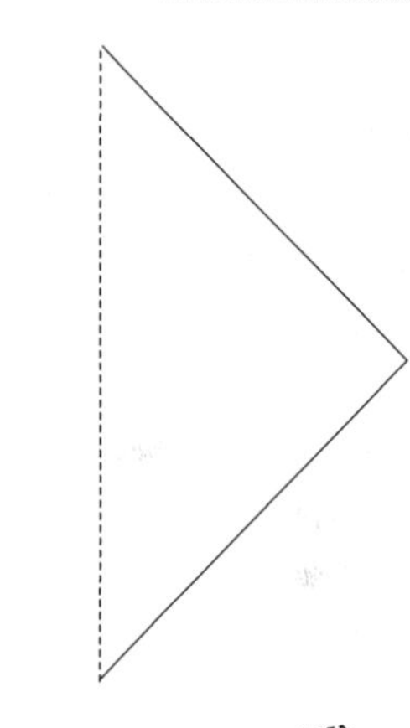

4. Fold the far corner of the napkin diagonally towards you and to the right so that the crease falls an inch or two short of the right-most corner. The newly formed point at the bottom should be a few inches to the right of the left one.

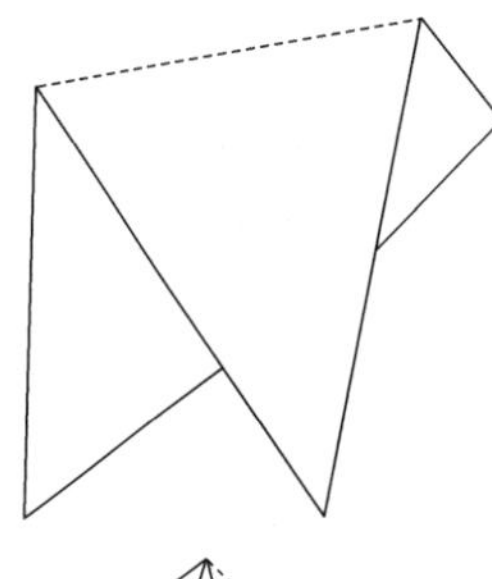

5. Fold the right-most point towards you, turning it at the same place as you did the last fold.

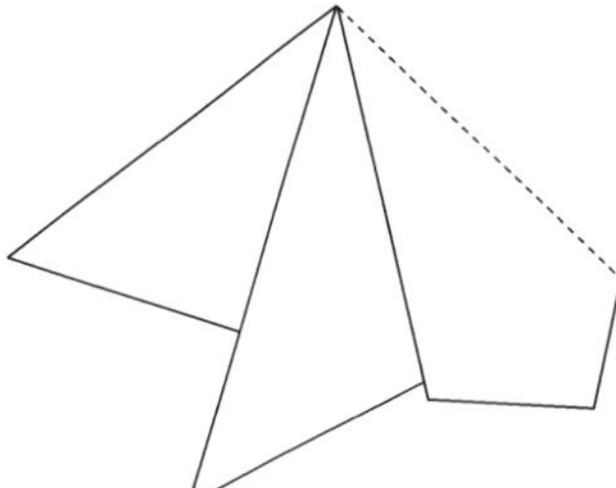

Appendix 2

Guidelines for writing a speech

- Know your audience – the people you are talking to.
- Plan your speech and write out a first draft.
- Write a good beginning to capture interest.
- Near the beginning of your speech outline what you are going to talk about, then cover each point in more detail.
- Include catchy phrases if you can.
- Keep to the point, don't repeat yourself and don't state the obvious.
- Have a good, definite ending. Often a good speech will refer back to a point that was made at the beginning.
- Read through the first draft of your speech and make any changes you think will improve the speech.
- Make sure your speech is clear and uses words that will be understood by your audience but don't make it so simple that they feel insulted.
- Make sure you say what you mean to say.
- Know yourself. If you are not naturally funny, don't put in jokes.
- Don't write anything that will insult or embarrass people.
- Don't try to flatter your audience too much.

Guidelines for giving a speech

- Practise your speech and try to learn it by heart.
- You could have your speech in front of you in large, clear print or handwriting, but don't actually read it, just glance at it from time to time.
- Wear clothes that look good and feel good. It is important to be comfortable and to look relaxed.
- Think about the way you look. Stand upright and face your audience, making sure you look confident.
- Give good eye contact and look at all sections of your audience in turn, moving your head slowly.
- Change your facial expression when necessary and don't be afraid to smile.
- Speak clearly and at a good speed – not too fast and not too slow and try not to stumble over your words.
- Vary the volume and tone of your speech to make it interesting, and try to emphasise important points, but don't shout.
- Be yourself. If you are not naturally funny, don't try to make people laugh.
- Don't sound as if you are apologising for being there by saying things like, "I hope you won't mind me saying a few words..."
- Don't go on too long and don't be boring.

Mapping

Jobs 1, pages 9–11

NC

English KS3

1.1a, b; 2.2a; 2.3a, k, o, s, t, u, v, w; 3.2j; 3.3e; 3.4a

English KS4

1.1a, b; 2.2a; 2.3b, m, n, o; 3.2k; 3.3e; 3.4d

Maths KS3

1.1a, b, c; 2.2l; 3.1a, b; 4d

Maths KS4

1.1a, b, c; 2.2l; 3.1b; 4d

PSHE Economic wellbeing and financial capability KS3

1.1a, c; 3b; 4a, g

PSHE Economic wellbeing and financial capability KS4

1.1a, c; 3a; 4a, h

Adult Core Curriculum

Rt/L1.1, Rt/L1.3, Rt/L1.5, Rw/L1.1, Rw/L1.2; Ws/L1.1, Ws/L1.2, Ws/L1.3, Ww/L1.1, Ww/L1.2

Jobs 2, page 12

NC

English KS3

1.1a, b, c, d, e; 1.4a, c, d; 2.1a, b, e, g, h, i; 2.2a, d; 2.3a, d, e, g, h, k, l, o, p, q, s, t, u, v, w; 3.1b, c, e; 3.2i; 3.3c, d, e; 3.4a, b; 4.1b, c, f; 4.3g, i

English KS4

1.1a, b, c, d, e; 1.4a, c, d; 2.1a, b, c, f, h, i, j; 2.2a, e; 2.3b, d, e, f, g, l, m, n, o; 3.1b, c, d; 3.2k; 3.3b, d, e; 3.4a, d; 4.1b, c, f; 4.3f, h

PSHE Personal wellbeing KS3

2.1b, d, f; 2.3a, c; 4c, d, e, f, h

PSHE Personal wellbeing KS4

2.1b, c, e; 2.3a, c; 4d, e, f, g, i

PSHE Economic wellbeing and financial capability KS3

1.1a, c; 3a, e; 4a, g

PSHE Economic wellbeing and financial capability KS4

1.1a, c; 3a, d; 4a, h

Adult Core Curriculum

SLlr/L1.1, SLlr/L1.2, SLlr/L1.3, SLlr/L1.4, SLlr/L1.5, SLlr/L1.6, SLc/L1.1, SLc/L1.2, SLc/L1.3, SLc/L1.4, SLd/L1.1, SLd/L1.2, SLd/L1.3, Rt/L1.1, Rt/L1.2, Rt/L1.3, Rt/L1.5, Rs/L1.1, Rs/L1.2, Rw/L1.1, Rw/L1.2, Rw/L1.3, Wt/L1.1, Wt/L1.2, Wt/L1.3, Wt/L1.4, Wt/L1.5, Wt/L1.6, Ws/L1.1, Ws/L1.2, Ws/L1.3, Ww/L1.1, Ww/L1.2

Interview 1, pages 13–14

NC

English KS3

1.1a; 2.1f, i; 2.3c, k, o, s, t, u, v, w; 3.1e; 3.2h; 3.3c, d; 3.4a; 4.1b, d, f; 4.3g

English KS4

1.1a; 2.1d, e, f; 2.3m, n, o; 3.1d; 3.2k; 3.3d, e; 3.4d; 4.1c, f, g; 4.3f

PSHE Economic wellbeing and financial capability KS3

1.1c; 3e; 4a, j

PSHE Economic wellbeing and financial capability KS4

1.1c; 3f; 4a, k

Adult Core Curriculum

SLlr/L1.1, SLlr/L1.2, SLlr/L1.3, SLlr/L1.4, SLlr/L1.5, SLlr/L1.6, SLc/L1.1, SLc/L1.2, SLc/L1.3, SLc/L1.4, SLd/L1.1, SLd/L1.2, SLd/L1.3, Ws/L1.1, Ws/L1.2, Ws/L1.3, Ww/L1.1, Ww/L1.2

Mapping

Interview 2, pages 15–16

NC

English KS3

1.1a; 2.1f, i; 2.3c, k, o, s, t, u, v, w; 3.1e; 3.2h; 3.3c, d; 3.4a; 4.1b, d, f; 4.3g

English KS4

1.1a; 2.1d, e, f; 2.3m, n, o; 3.1d; 3.2k; 3.3d, e; 3.4d; 4.1c, f, g; 4.3f

PSHE Economic wellbeing and financial capability KS3

1.1c; 3e; 4a, j

PSHE Economic wellbeing and financial capability KS4

1.1c; 3f; 4a, k

Adult Core Curriculum

SLlr/L1.1, SLlr/L1.2, SLlr/L1.3, SLlr/L1.4, SLlr/L1.5, SLlr/L1.6, SLc/L1.1, SLc/L1.2, SLc/L1.3, SLc/L1.4, SLd/L1.1, SLd/L1.2, SLd/L1.3,Ws/L1.1, Ws/L1.2, Ws/L1.3, Ww/L1.1, Ww/L1.2

Interview 3, pages 17–19

NC

English KS3

1.1a; 2.1f, i; 1.4c, d; 2.1b, e, g, h; 2.3c, k, o, s, t, u, v, w; 3.1b, e; 3.2h; 3.3c, d; 3.4a; 4.1b, d, e, f; 4.3g

English KS4

1.1a; 1.4c, d; 2.1a, b, d, e, f, h, i, j; 2.3m, n, o; 3.1b, d; 3.2k; 3.3d, e; 3.4d; 4.1b, c, f, g; 4.3f

PSHE Personal wellbeing KS3

2.3c; 4d, e, h

PSHE Personal wellbeing KS4

2.3c; 4b, e, f, i

PSHE Economic wellbeing and financial capability KS3

1.1c; 3e; 4a, j

PSHE Economic wellbeing and financial capability KS4

1.1c; 3f; 4a, k

Adult Core Curriculum

SLlr/L1.1, SLlr/L1.2, SLlr/L1.3, SLlr/L1.4, SLlr/L1.5, SLlr/L1.6, SLc/L1.1, SLc/L1.2, SLc/L1.3, SLc/L1.4, SLd/L1.1, SLd/L1.2, SLd/L1.3, Ws/L1.1, Ws/L1.2, Ws/L1.3, Ww/L1.1, Ww/L1.2

Just the job?, pages 20–26

NC

English KS3

1.1a, b; 2.2a; 2.3a, g, h, k, l, o, s, t, u, v, w; 3.2j; 3.3c, d, e; 3.4a; 4.3g

English KS4

1.1a, b; 2.2a; 2.3b, e, f, g, m, n, o; 3.2k; 3.3c, d, e; 3.4d; 4.3f

Maths KS3

1.1a, b, c; 2.2l; 3.1a, b; 4d

Maths KS4

1.1a, b, c; 2.2l; 3.1b; 4d

PSHE Economic wellbeing and financial capability KS3

1.1a, c; 3b; 4a, g

PSHE Economic wellbeing and financial capability KS4

1.1a, c; 3a; 4a, h

Adult Core Curriculum

Rt/L1.1, Rt/L1.3, Rt/L1.5, Rw/L1.1, Rw/L1.2, Wt/L1.1, Wt/L1.2, Wt/L1.3, Wt/L1.4, Wt/L1.5, Wt/L1.6, Ws/L1.1, Ws/L1.2, Ws/L1.3, Ww/L1.1, Ww/L1.2

Mapping

Wages, pages 27–28

NC

English KS3

1.1a, d, e; 2.1a, b, c, e, g; 2.3s, w; 3.1b, e; 4.1b, f

English KS4

1.1a, d, e; 2.1a, b, c, f, h, j; 2.3m, o; 4.1b, c, f

Maths KS3

1.1a, b, c; 2.2l; 3.1a, b; 4d

Maths KS4

1.1a, b, c; 2.2l; 3.1b; 4d

PSHE Economic wellbeing and financial capability KS3

1.2b; 2.4c

PSHE Economic wellbeing and financial capability KS4

1.2b; 2.4c

Adult Core Curriculum

SLlr/L1.1, SLlr/L1.2, SLlr/L1.3, SLlr/L1.4, SLlr/L1.5, SLlr/L1.6, SLc/L1.1, SLc/L1.2, SLc/L1.3, SLc/L1.4, SLd/L1.1, SLd/L1.2, SLd/L1.3, Rs/L1.1, Rs/L1.2, Rs/L1.3, Rw/L1.1, Rw/L1.2

A fair wage?, pages 29–30

NC

English KS3

1.1a, d, e; 2.1a, b, c, e, g; 2.3s, w; 3.1b, e; 4.1b, f

English KS4

1.1a, d, e; 2.1a, b, c, f, h, j; 2.3m, o; 4.1b, c, f

Maths KS3

1.1a, b, c; 2.2l; 3.1a, b; 4d

Maths KS4

1.1a, b, c; 2.2l; 3.1b; 4d

Adult Core Curriculum

SLlr/L1.1, SLlr/L1.2, SLlr/L1.3, SLlr/L1.4, SLlr/L1.5, SLlr/L1.6, SLc/L1.1, SLc/L1.2, SLc/L1.3, SLc/L1.4, SLd/L1.1, SLd/L1.2, SLd/L1.3, Rw/L1.1, Rw/L1.2, Ws/L1.1, Ws/L1.2, Ws/L1.3, Ww/L1.1, Ww/L1.2, N1/L1.1, MSS1/L1.1, MSS1/L1.3

Talking, page 31

NC

English KS3

1.1a, d, e; 2.1a, e, f, g, h, i; 3.1b, e; 4.1b, d, e, f

English KS4

1.1a, d, e; 2.1a, b, c, d, e, f, g, h, i, j; 3.1b, d; 4.1b, c, d, f, g

PSHE Personal wellbeing KS3

2.3c; 4c, e

PSHE Personal wellbeing KS4

2.3c; 4b, d, f

PSHE Economic wellbeing and financial capability KS3

1.1c; 3b; 4a, j

PSHE Economic wellbeing and financial capability KS4

1.1c; 3f; 4a, k

Adult Core Curriculum

SLlr/L1.1, SLlr/L1.2, SLlr/L1.3, SLlr/L1.4, SLlr/L1.5, SLlr/L1.6, SLc/L1.1, SLc/L1.2, SLc/L1.3, SLc/L1.4, SLd/L1.1, SLd/L1.2, SLd/L1.3, Rw/L1.2, Rw/L1.3, Ww/L1.1, Ww/L1.2

Literacy levels at work, pages 32–34

NC

English KS3

1.1a, b, c, d, e; 1.4a, c, d; 2.1a, b, e, g, h, i; 2.2a, d; 2.3a, d, e, g, h, k, l, o, p, q, s, t, u, v, w; 3.1b, c, e; 3.2i; 3.3c, d, e; 3.4a, b; 4.1b, c, f; 4.3g, i

Mapping

English KS4

1.1a, b, c, d, e; 1.4a, c, d; 2.1a, b, c, f, h, i, j; 2.2a, e; 2.3b, d, e, f, g, l, m, n, o; 3.1b, c, d; 3.2k; 3.3b, d, e; 3.4a, d; 4.1b, c, f; 4.3f, h

Adult Core Curriculum

SLlr/L1.1, SLlr/L1.2, SLlr/L1.3, SLlr/L1.4, SLlr/L1.5, SLlr/L1.6, SLc/L1.1, SLc/L1.2, SLc/L1.3, SLc/L1.4, SLd/L1.1, SLd/L1.2, SLd/L1.3, Rt/L1.1, Rt/L1.3, Rt/L1.5, Rs/L1.1, Rs/L1.2, Rw/L1.2, Rw/L1.3, Wt/L1.1, Wt/L1.2, Wt/L1.3, Wt/L1.4, Wt/L1.5, Wt/L1.6, Ws/L1.1, Ws/L1.2, Ws/L1.3, Ww/L1.1, Ww/L1.2

Magic, page 35

NC

English KS3

1.1a, d, e; 2.1a, e, f, g, h, i; 3.1b, e; 4.1b, d, e

English KS4

1.1a, d, e; 2.1a, b, c, d, e, f, g, h, i, j; 3.1b, d; 4.1b, c, d, f

Adult Core Curriculum

SLlr/L1.1, SLlr/L1.2, SLlr/L1.3, SLlr/L1.4, SLlr/L1.5, SLlr/L1.6, SLc/L1.1, SLc/L1.2, SLc/L1.3, SLc/L1.4, SLd/L1.1, SLd/L1.2, SLd/L1.3

Menu, page 36

NC

English KS3

1.1a, d, e; 2.1a, b, c, e, g; 2.3a, d, g, k, p, q, s, t, u, v, w; 3.1e; 3.3d, e; 3.4a; 4.1b, e

English KS4

1.1a, d, e; 2.1e, f; 2.3b, e, l, m, n, o; 3.1d; 3.3d, e; 3.4d; 4.1c

Design and technology KS3

2b; 4c

Adult Core Curriculum

SLlr/L1.1, SLlr/L1.2, Rw/L1.2, Rw/L1.3, Wt/L1.1, Wt/L1.2, Wt/L1.3, Wt/L1.4, Wt/L1.5, Wt/L1.6, Ws/L1.1, Ws/L1.2, Ws/L1.3, Ww/L1.1, Ww/L1.2

Following instructions – know your napkins, page 37

NC

English KS3

1.1a; 2.1e, i; 2.3a, s, t, u, w; 3.1e; 4.1b, d

English KS4

1.1a; 2.1d, e, f; 2.3m, n, o; 3.1d; 4.1c, g

PSHE Personal wellbeing KS3

4f

PSHE Personal wellbeing KS4

4g

Adult Core Curriculum

SLlr/L1.1, SLlr/L1.2, Rs/L1.2, Rs/L1.3, Ws/L1.1, Ws/L1.2, Ws/L1.3, Ww/L1.1, Ww/L1.2

Following instructions – serviette style, page 38

NC

English KS3

1.1a, d, e; 2.1a, b, c, e, g; 2.3a, d, g, k, p, q, s, t, u, v, w; 3.1e; 3.3d, e; 3.4a; 4.1b, e

English KS4

1.1a, d, e; 2.1e, f; 2.3b, e, l, m, n, o; 3.1d; 3.3d, e; 3.4d; 4.1c

PSHE Personal wellbeing KS3

2.3c; 4c, e, f

PSHE Personal wellbeing KS4

2.3c; 4b, d, f, g

Mapping

Adult Core Curriculum

SLlr/L1.1, SLlr/L1.2, Rs/L1.2, Rs/L1.3, Ws/L1.1, Ws/L1.2, Ws/L1.3, Ww/L1.1, Ww/L1.2

Darts, page 39

NC

English KS3

1.1a, c, d, e; 2.1a, b, c, d, e, f, g, h, i; 2.3a, b, d, g, h, j, k, o, p, s, t, u, v, w; 3.1b, c, d, e; 3.2h; 3.3c, e; 3.4a; 4.1b, c, d, e, f

English KS4

1.1a, c, d, e; 2.1a, b, c, d, e, f, g, h, i, j; 2.3b, g, m, n, o; 3.1b, c, d; 3.2j; 3.3c, d, e; 3.4d; 4.1b, c, d, g; 4.3e

PSHE Personal wellbeing KS3

2.1b; 2.3c; 4c, d, e, f

PSHE Personal wellbeing KS4

2.1b; 2.3c; 4b, d, e, f, g

Adult Core Curriculum

SLlr/L1.1, SLlr/L1.2, SLc/L1.1, SLc/L1.3, SLc/L1.4, Rw/L1.2, Rw/L1.3, Wt/L1.2, Wt/L1.3, Wt/L1.4, Wt/L1.5, Wt/L1.6, Ws/L1.1, Ws/L1.2, Ws/L1.3, Ww/L1.1, Ww/L1.2

Introducing Z Factor, pages 40–42

NC

English KS3

1.1a, b, c, e; 2.2a, b; 2.3k, s, t, u, v, w; 3.2i; 3.3c, d, e

English KS4

1.1a, b, c, e; 2.2a; 2.3m, n, o; 3.2k; 3.3c, d, e

Adult Core Curriculum

Rt/L1.1, Rt/L1.2, Rt/L1.3, Rt/L1.4, Rt/L1.5, Rs/L1.1, Rs/L1.2, Rw/L1.2, Rw/L1.3, Ws/L1.1, Ws/L1.2, Ws/L1.3, Ww/L1.1, Ww/L1.2

Finish the lyrics, page 43

NC

English KS3

1.1a, b, c, d, e; 1.2a, b; 2.1a, e, f, g, h, i; 2.2a, b, j, n; 2.3a, b, c, d, e, f, g, p, q, s, w; 3.1b, e; 3.3a, e; 4.1a, b, c, d, e; 4.3c, e

English KS4

1.1a, b, c, d, e; 1.2a, b; 2.1a, d, f, h, i, j; 2.2a, l; 2.3a, b, f, o; 3.1b, d; 3.3a, c, e; 4.1b, c; 4.3c, e

PSHE Personal wellbeing KS3

2.1b; 2.3c; 4c, d, e, f

PSHE Personal wellbeing KS4

2.1b; 2.3c; 4b, d, e, f, g

Adult Core Curriculum

SLlr/L1.1, SLlr/L1.2, SLlr/L1.3, SLlr/L1.4, SLlr/L1.5, SLlr/L1.6, SLc/L1.1, SLc/L1.2, SLc/L1.3, SLc/L1.4, SLd/L1.1, SLd/L1.2, SLd/L1.3, Rw/L1.2, Rw/L1.3, Wt/L1.1, Wt/L1.4, Wt/L1.5, Wt/L1.6, Ws/L1.1, Ws/L1.2, Ws/L1.3, Ww/L1.1, Ww/L1.2

Breaking news, pages 44–46

NC

English KS3

1.1a, b, c, d, e; 1.4a, c, d; 2.1a, b, e, g, h, i; 2.2a, d; 2.3a, d, e, g, h, k, l, o, p, q, s, t, u, v, w; 3.1b, c, e; 3.2i; 3.3c, d, e; 3.4a, b; 4.1b, c, f; 4.3g, i

English KS4

1.1a, b, c, d, e; 1.4a, c, d; 2.1a, b, c, f, h, i, j; 2.2a, e; 2.3b, d, e, f, g, l, m, n, o; 3.1b, c, d; 3.2k; 3.3b, d, e; 3.4a, d; 4.1b, c, f; 4.3f, h

PSHE Personal wellbeing KS3

2.1b, d, f; 2.3a, c; 4c, d, e, f, h

PSHE Personal wellbeing KS4

2.1b, c, e; 2.3a, c; 4d, e, f, g, i

Mapping

PSHE Economic wellbeing and financial capability KS3

1.1a, c; 3a, e; 4a, g

PSHE Economic wellbeing and financial capability KS4

1.1a, c; 3a, d; 4a, h

Adult Core Curriculum

SLlr/L1.1, SLlr/L1.2, SLlr/L1.3, SLlr/L1.4, SLlr/L1.5, SLlr/L1.6, SLc/L1.1, SLc/L1.2, SLc/L1.3, SLc/L1.4, SLd/L1.1, SLd/L1.2, SLd/L1.3, Rt/L1.1, Rt/L1.2, Rt/L1.3, Rt/L1.5, Rs/L1.1, Rs/L1.2, Rw/L1.1, Rw/L1.2, Rw/L1.3, Wt/L1.1, Wt/L1.2, Wt/L1.3, Wt/L1.4, Wt/L1.5, Wt/L1.6, Ws/L1.1, Ws/L1.2, Ws/L1.3, Ww/L1.1, Ww/L1.2

News headlines, page 47

NC

English KS3

1.1a, b, c, d, e; 1.4a, c, d; 2.1a, b, d, e, g, h, i; 2.2a, d; 2.3a, d, e, g, h, k, l, o, p, q, s, t, u, v, w; 3.1b, c, e; 3.2i; 3.3c, d, e; 3.4a, b; 4.1b, c, e, f; 4.3g, i

English KS4

1.1a, b, c, d, e; 1.4a, c, d; 2.1a, b, c, f, g, h, i, j; 2.2a, e; 2.3b, d, e, f, g, l, m, n, o; 3.1b, c, d; 3.2k; 3.3b, d, e; 3.4a, d; 4.1b, c, d, f; 4.3f, h

PSHE Personal wellbeing KS3

2.1b, d, f; 2.3a, c; 4c, d, e, f, h

PSHE Personal wellbeing KS4

2.1b, c, e; 2.3a, c; 4d, e, f, g, i

PSHE Economic wellbeing and financial capability KS3

1.1a, c; 3a, e; 4a, g

PSHE Economic wellbeing and financial capability KS4

1.1a, c; 3a, d; 4a, h

Adult Core Curriculum

SLlr/L1.1, SLlr/L1.2, SLlr/L1.3, SLlr/L1.4, SLlr/L1.5, SLlr/L1.6, SLc/L1.1, SLc/L1.2, SLc/L1.3, SLc/L1.4, SLd/L1.1, SLd/L1.2, SLd/L1.3, Wt/L1.1, Wt/L1.2, Wt/L1.3, Wt/L1.4, Wt/L1.5, Wt/L1.6, Ws/L1.1, Ws/L1.2, Ws/L1.3, Ww/L1.1, Ww/L1.2

Picture this, pages 48–49

NC

English KS3

2.3a, k, s, t, u, v, w; 3.3d, e

English KS4

2.3b, m, n, o; 3.3d, e

Adult Core Curriculum

Rw/L1.2, Rw/L1.3, Ws/L1.1, Ws/L1.2, Ws/L1.3, Ww/L1.1, Ww/L1.2

Picture that, pages 50–51

NC

English KS3

1.1a; 2.1a, b; 3.1b, e; 4.1b, d

English KS4

1.1a; 2.1a, b, e, f; 3.1b, d; 4.1b, c

Adult Core Curriculum

SLlr/L1.1, SLlr/L1.2, SLc/L1.1, SLc/L1.3, SLc/L1.4, SLd/L1.1, SLd/L1.2, SLd/L1.3, Rw/L1.2, Rw/L1.3

Picture these, pages 52–54

NC

English KS3

1.1a; 2.3w

English KS4

1.1a; 2.3o

Adult Core Curriculum

Rw/L1.2, Rw/L1.3, Ww/L1.1, Ww/L1.2

Mapping

The Daily Blag, pages 55–56

NC

English KS3

1.1b; 2.2a, b; 3.2h

English KS4

1.1b, d; 2.2a; 3.2i

Adult Core Curriculum

Rt/L1.1, Rs/L1.1, Rs/L1.2, Rw/L1.2, Rw/L1.3

Pedalo power, pages 57–58

NC

English KS3

1.1a, b, c, d, e; 1.4a, c, d; 2.1a, b, e, g, h, i; 2.2a, d; 2.3a, d, e, g, h, k, l, o, p, q, s, t, u, v, w; 3.1b, c, e; 3.2i; 3.3c, d, e; 3.4a, b; 4.1b, c, f; 4.3g, i

English KS4

1.1a, b, c, d, e; 1.4a, c, d; 2.1a, b, c, f, h, i, j; 2.2a, e; 2.3b, d, e, f, g, l, m, n, o; 3.1b, c, d; 3.2k; 3.3b, d, e; 3.4a, d; 4.1b, c, f; 4.3f, h

PSHE Personal wellbeing KS3

2.3c; 4c, e

PSHE Personal wellbeing KS4

2.3c; 4d, f

Adult Core Curriculum

SLlr/L1.1, SLlr/L1.2, SLlr/L1.3, SLlr/L1.4, SLlr/L1.5, SLlr/L1.6, SLc/L1.1, SLc/L1.2, SLc/L1.3, SLc/L1.4, SLd/L1.1, SLd/L1.2, SLd/L1.3, Rw/L1.2, Rw/L1.3, Wt/L1.4, Ws/L1.1, Ws/L1.2, Ws/L1.3, Ww/L1.1, Ww/L1.2

The fishing line, page 59

NC

English KS3

1.1a, b, c, d, e; 1.4a, c, d; 2.1a, b, e, g, h, i; 2.2a, d; 2.3a, d, e, g, h, k, l, o, p, q, s, t, u, v, w; 3.1b, c, e; 3.2i; 3.3c, d, e; 3.4a, b; 4.1b, c, f; 4.3g, i

English KS4

1.1a, b, c, d, e; 1.4a, c, d; 2.1a, b, c, f, h, i, j; 2.2a, e; 2.3b, d, e, f, g, l, m, n, o; 3.1b, c, d; 3.2k; 3.3b, d, e; 3.4a, d; 4.1b, c, f; 4.3f, h

PSHE Personal wellbeing KS3

2.3c; 4c, e

PSHE Personal wellbeing KS4

2.3c; 4d, f

Adult Core Curriculum

SLlr/L1.1, SLlr/L1.2, SLlr/L1.3, SLlr/L1.4, SLlr/L1.5, SLlr/L1.6, SLc/L1.1, SLc/L1.2, SLc/L1.3, SLc/L1.4, SLd/L1.1, SLd/L1.2, SLd/L1.3, Rw/L1.2, Rw/L1.3, Wt/L1.1, Wt/L1.2, Wt/L1.3, Wt/L1.4, Wt/L1.5, Wt/L1.6, Ws/L1.1, Ws/L1.2, Ws/L1.3, Ww/L1.1, Ww/L1.2

Public speaking, pages 60–61

NC

English KS3

1.1a, b, c, d, e; 1.4a, c, d; 2.1a, b, e, g, h, i; 2.2a, d; 2.3a, d, e, g, h, k, l, o, p, q, s, t, u, v, w; 3.1b, c, e; 3.2i; 3.3c, d, e; 3.4a, b; 4.1b, c, f; 4.3g, i

English KS4

1.1a, b, c, d, e; 1.4a, c, d; 2.1a, b, c, f, h, i, j; 2.2a, e; 2.3b, d, e, f, g, l, m, n, o; 3.1b, c, d; 3.2k; 3.3b, d, e; 3.4a, d; 4.1b, c, f; 4.3f, h

PSHE Personal wellbeing KS3

2.3c; 4c, e

PSHE Personal wellbeing KS4

2.3c; 4d, f

Mapping

Adult Core Curriculum

SLlr/L1.1, SLlr/L1.2, SLlr/L1.3, SLlr/L1.4, SLlr/L1.5, SLlr/L1.6, SLc/L1.1, SLc/L1.2, SLc/L1.3, SLc/L1.4, SLd/L1.1, SLd/L1.2, SLd/L1.3, Rw/L1.2, Rw/L1.3, Wt/L1.4, Ws/L1.1, Ws/L1.2, Ws/L1.3, Ww/L1.1, Ww/L1.2

Speaking in public, pages 62–65

NC

English KS3

1.1a, b, c, d, e; 1.4a, c, d; 2.1a, b, e, g, h, i; 2.2a, d; 2.3a, d, e, g, h, k, l, o, p, q, s, t, u, v, w; 3.1b, c, e; 3.2i; 3.3c, d, e; 3.4a, b; 4.1b, c, f; 4.3g, i

English KS4

1.1a, b, c, d, e; 1.4a, c, d; 2.1a, b, c, f, h, i, j; 2.2a, e; 2.3b, d, e, f, g, l, m, n, o; 3.1b, c, d; 3.2k; 3.3b, d, e; 3.4a, d; 4.1b, c, f; 4.3f, h

PSHE Personal wellbeing KS3

2.3c; 4c, e

PSHE Personal wellbeing KS4

2.3c; 4d, f

Adult Core Curriculum

SLlr/L1.1, SLlr/L1.2, SLlr/L1.3, SLlr/L1.4, SLlr/L1.5, SLlr/L1.6, SLc/L1.1, SLc/L1.2, SLc/L1.3, SLc/L1.4, SLd/L1.1, SLd/L1.2, SLd/L1.3, Rt/L1.1, Rt/L1.3, Rt/L1.5, Rs/L1.1, Rs/L1.2, Rw/L1.2, Rw/L1.3, Wt/L1.1, Wt/L1.2, Wt/L1.3, Wt/L1.4, Wt/L1.5, Wt/L1.6, Ws/L1.1, Ws/L1.2, Ws/L1.3, Ww/L1.1, Ww/L1.2

Listen carefully, page 66

NC

English KS3

1.1a, b, c, d, e; 1.4a, c, d; 2.1a, b, e, g, h, i; 2.2a, d; 2.3a, d, e, g, h, k, l, o, p, q, s, t, u, v, w; 3.1b, c, e; 3.2i; 3.3c, d, e; 3.4a, b; 4.1b, c, f; 4.3g, i

English KS4

1.1a, b, c, d, e; 1.4a, c, d; 2.1a, b, c, f, h, i, j; 2.2a, e; 2.3b, d, e, f, g, l, m, n, o; 3.1b, c, d; 3.2k; 3.3b, d, e; 3.4a, d; 4.1b, c, f; 4.3f, h

PSHE Personal wellbeing KS3

2.3c; 4c, e

PSHE Personal wellbeing KS4

2.3c; 4d, f

Adult Core Curriculum

SLlr/L1.1, SLlr/L1.2, SLlr/L1.3, SLlr/L1.4, SLlr/L1.5, SLlr/L1.6, SLc/L1.1, SLc/L1.2, SLc/L1.3, SLc/L1.4, SLd/L1.1, SLd/L1.2, SLd/L1.3, Rw/L1.2, Rw/L1.3, Wt/L1.1, Wt/L1.2, Wt/L1.3, Wt/L1.4, Wt/L1.5, Wt/L1.6, Ws/L1.1, Ws/L1.2, Ws/L1.3, Ww/L1.1, Ww/L1.2

Customer care 1, pages 67–68

NC

English KS3

1.1a, b, c, d, e; 1.4a, c, d; 2.1a, b, e, g, h, i; 2.2a, d; 2.3a, d, e, g, h, k, l, o, p, q, s, t, u, v, w; 3.1b, c, e; 3.2i; 3.3c, d, e; 3.4a, b; 4.1b, c, f; 4.3g, i

English KS4

1.1a, b, c, d, e; 1.4a, c, d; 2.1a, b, c, f, h, i, j; 2.2a, e; 2.3b, d, e, f, g, l, m, n, o; 3.1b, c, d; 3.2k; 3.3b, d, e; 3.4a, d; 4.1b, c, f; 4.3f, h

PSHE Personal wellbeing KS3

2.3c; 4c, e

PSHE Personal wellbeing KS4

2.3c; 4d, f

Adult Core Curriculum

SLlr/L1.1, SLlr/L1.2, SLlr/L1.3, SLlr/L1.4, SLlr/L1.5, SLlr/L1.6, SLc/L1.1, SLc/L1.2, SLc/L1.3, SLc/L1.4, SLd/L1.1, SLd/L1.2, SLd/L1.3, Rw/L1.2, Rw/L1.3, Wt/L1.1, Wt/L1.2, Wt/L1.3, Wt/L1.4, Wt/L1.5, Wt/L1.6, Ws/L1.1, Ws/L1.2, Ws/L1.3, Ww/L1.1, Ww/L1.2

Mapping

Customer care 2, pages 69–70

NC

English KS3

1.1a, b, c, d, e; 1.4a, c, d; 2.1a, b, e, g, h, i; 2.2a, d; 2.3a, d, e, g, h, k, l, o, p, q, s, t, u, v, w; 3.1b, c, e; 3.2i; 3.3c, d, e; 3.4a, b; 4.1b, c, f; 4.3g, i

English KS4

1.1a, b, c, d, e; 1.4a, c, d; 2.1a, b, c, f, h, i, j; 2.2a, e; 2.3b, d, e, f, g, l, m, n, o; 3.1b, c, d; 3.2k; 3.3b, d, e; 3.4a, d; 4.1b, c, f; 4.3f, h

PSHE Personal wellbeing KS3

2.3c; 4c, e

PSHE Personal wellbeing KS4

2.3c; 4d, f

Adult Core Curriculum

SLlr/L1.1, SLlr/L1.2, SLlr/L1.3, SLlr/L1.4, SLlr/L1.5, SLlr/L1.6, SLc/L1.1, SLc/L1.2, SLc/L1.3, SLc/L1.4, SLd/L1.1, SLd/L1.2, SLd/L1.3, Rw/L1.2, Rw/L1.3, Wt/L1.1, Wt/L1.2, Wt/L1.3, Wt/L1.4, Wt/L1.5, Wt/L1.6, Ws/L1.1, Ws/L1.2, Ws/L1.3, Ww/L1.1, Ww/L1.2

Customer care 3, pages 71–72

NC

English KS3

1.1a, b; 2.2a, b; 2.3a, d, e, g, h, k, l, o, q, s, t, u, v, w; 3.2i; 3.3c, d, e; 3.4a; 4.3i

English KS4

1.1a, b, d; 2.2a; 2.3b, d, e, f, g, l, m, n, o; 3.2j; 3.3d, e; 3.4d; 4.3h

Adult Core Curriculum

Rt.L1.1, Rt/L1.2, Rt/L1.3, Rt/L1.5, Rs/L1.1, Rs/L1.2, Rw/L1.2, Rw/L1.3, Wt/L1.1, Wt/L1.2, Wt/L1.3, Wt/L1.4, Wt/L1.5, Wt/L1.6, Ws/L1.1, Ws/L1.2, Ws/L1.3, Ww/L1.1, Ww/L1.2

Phone calls, page 73

NC

English KS3

1.1a, b, c, d, e; 1.4a, c, d; 2.1a, b, e, g, h, i; 2.2a, d; 2.3a, d, e, g, h, k, l, o, p, q, s, t, u, v, w; 3.1b, c, e; 3.2i; 3.3c, d, e; 3.4a, b; 4.1b, c, f; 4.3g, i

English KS4

1.1a, b, c, d, e; 1.4a, c, d; 2.1a, b, c, f, h, i, j; 2.2a, e; 2.3b, d, e, f, g, l, m, n, o; 3.1b, c, d; 3.2k; 3.3b, d, e; 3.4a, d; 4.1b, c, f; 4.3f, h

PSHE Personal wellbeing KS3

2.3c; 4c, e

PSHE Personal wellbeing KS4

2.3c; 4d, f

Adult Core Curriculum

SLlr/L1.1, SLlr/L1.2, SLlr/L1.3, SLlr/L1.4, SLlr/L1.5, SLlr/L1.6, SLc/L1.1, SLc/L1.2, SLc/L1.3, SLc/L1.4, SLd/L1.1, SLd/L1.2, SLd/L1.3, Rw/L1.2, Rw/L1.3, Ws/L1.1, Ws/L1.2, Ws/L1.3, Ww/L1.1, Ww/L1.2

Satisfied customers, pages 74–76

NC

English KS3

1.1a, d, e; 2.1a, e, g, h, i; 2.2a; 2.3a, k, s, t, u, w; 3.1b, e; 3.3c, e; 3.4a; 4.1b, c, e, f; 4.3g

English KS4

1.1a, b, d; 2.1a, b, c, f, h, i, j; 2.2a; 2.3b, m, o; 3.1b, d; 3.3d, e; 3.4d; 4.1b, c, d, f; 4.3f

PSHE Personal wellbeing KS3

2.3c; 4c, e, h

PSHE Personal wellbeing KS4

2.3c; 4b, d, f, i

Mapping

Adult Core Curriculum

SLlr/L1.1, SLlr/L1.2, SLlr/L1.3, SLlr/L1.4, SLlr/L1.5, SLlr/L1.6, SLc/L1.1, SLc/L1.3, SLd/L1.1, SLd/L1.2, SLd/L1.3, Rw/L1.2, Rw/L1.3, Ws/L1.1, Ws/L1.2, Ws/L1.3, Ww/L1.1, Ww/L1.2

Help!, pages 77–78

NC

English KS3

1.1a, b, c, d, e; 1.4a, c, d; 2.1a, b, e, g, h, i; 2.2a, d; 2.3a, d, e, g, h, k, l, o, p, q, s, t, u, v, w; 3.1b, c, e; 3.3c, d, e; 3.4a, b; 4.1b, c, f; 4.3g, i

English KS4

1.1a, b, c, d, e; 1.4a, c, d; 2.1a, b, c, f, h, i, j; 2.2a, e; 2.3b, d, e, f, g, l, m, n, o; 3.1b, c, d; 3.3b, d, e; 3.4a, d; 4.1b, c, f; 4.3f, h

PSHE Personal wellbeing KS3

2.3c; 4c, e

PSHE Personal wellbeing KS4

2.3c; 4d, f

Adult Core Curriculum

SLlr/L1.1, SLlr/L1.2, SLlr/L1.3, SLlr/L1.4, SLlr/L1.5, SLlr/L1.6, SLc/L1.1, SLc/L1.2, SLc/L1.3, SLc/L1.4, SLd/L1.1, SLd/L1.2, SLd/L1.3, Rw/L1.2, Rw/L1.3, Wt/L1.1, Wt/L1.2, Wt/L1.3, Wt/L1.4, Wt/L1.5, Wt/L1.6, Ws/L1.1, Ws/L1.2, Ws/L1.3, Ww/L1.1, Ww/L1.2

The boss blunders, pages 79–80

NC

English KS3

1.1a, b, c, d, e; 1.4a; 2.1a, e, g, h, i; 2.a; 2.3a, d, g, k, o, p, q, s, t, u, v, w; 3.1b, e; 3.2i; 3.3d, e; 3.4a; 4.1b, e

English KS4

1.1a, b, c, d, e; 1.4a; 2.1a, b, f, h, i, j; 2.2a; 2.3b, m, n, o; 3.1b, d; 3.2k; 3.3d, e; 3.4d; 4.1b, c

PSHE Personal wellbeing KS3

2.1b; 2.3c; 4e, f

PSHE Personal wellbeing KS4

2.1b; 2.3c; 4b, f, g

Adult Core Curriculum

SLlr/L1.1, SLlr/L1.2, SLlr/L1.3, SLlr/L1.4, SLlr/L1.5, SLlr/L1.6, SLc/L1.1, SLc/L1.3, SLd/L1.1, SLd/L1.2, SLd/L1.3, Rs/L1.1, Rs/L1.2, Rw/L1.2, Rw/L1.3, Wt/L1.1, Wt/L1.3, Wt/L1.5, Ws/L1.1, Ws/L1.2, Ws/L1.3, Ww/L1.1, Ww/L1.2

A phone call from the boss, pages 81–82

NC

English KS3

1.1a; 2.1e, f, g; 2.3k, o, p, s, t, u, v, w; 3.1b, d, e; 3.3c, d, e; 4.1b, c, f; 4.3g

English KS4

1.1a; 2.1b, e, f, g, h, i, j; 2.3b, m, n, o; 3.1b, d; 3.3c, d, e; 4.1a, b, c, d, f, g; 4.3f

PSHE Economic wellbeing and financial capability KS3

1.1c; 2.1c; 3e; 4a, j

PSHE Economic wellbeing and financial capability KS4

1.1c; 2.1c; 3f; 4a, k

PSHE Personal wellbeing KS3

2.3c; 2.1b; 4c, e, f, h

PSHE Personal wellbeing KS4

2.1b; 2.3c; 4d, f, g, i

Adult Core Curriculum

SLlr/L1.1, SLlr/L1.2, SLlr/L1.3, SLlr/L1.4, SLlr/L1.5, SLlr/L1.6, SLc/L1.1, SLc/L1.2, SLc/L1.3, SLc/L1.4, SLd/L1.1, SLd/L1.2, SLd/L1.3, Rw/L1.2, Rw/L1.3, Wt/L1.1, Wt/L1.2, Wt/L1.3, Wt/L1.4, Wt/L1.5, Ws/L1.1, Ws/L1.2, Ws/L1.3, Ww/L1.1, Ww/L1.2

Mapping

When things go wrong, pages 83–85

NC

English KS3

1.1a; 2.1i; 2.2a; 2.3a, w; 3.3c, d, e; 4.1b

English KS4

1.1a; 2.1f; 2.2a; 2.3b, o; 3.3c, e; 4.1c

PSHE Economic wellbeing and financial capability KS3

4a

PSHE Economic wellbeing and financial capability KS4

4a

Adult Core Curriculum

Rt/L1.3, Rt/L1.5, Rs/L1.1, Rs/L1.2, Rw/L1.2, Rw/L1.3, Wt/L1.1, Wt/L1.2, Wt/L1.3, Wt/L1.5, Ws/L1.1, Ws/L1.2, Ws/L1.3, Ww/L1.1, Ww/L1.2

Eyewitness, pages 86–88

NC

English KS3

1.1a, b, d, e; 2.1a, b, c, e, f, g, h, i; 2.2a; 2.3s, t, u, v, w; 3.1b, c, e; 3.2j; 3.3d, e; 4.1b, c, e, f; 4.3g

English KS4

1.1a, c, d; 2.1a, b, c, e, f, g, h, i, j; 2.2a; 2.3m, n, o; 3.1b, c, d; 3.2k; 3.3c, e; 4.1b, c, f; 4.3f

PSHE Personal wellbeing KS3

2.3c; 4c, e

PSHE Personal wellbeing KS4

2.3c; 4e, f

Adult Core Curriculum

SLlr/L1.1, SLlr/L1.2, SLlr/L1.3, SLlr/L1.4, SLlr/L1.5, SLlr/L1.6, SLc/L1.1, SLc/L1.2, SLc/L1.3, SLc/L1.4, SLd/L1.1, SLd/L1.2, SLd/L1.3, Rw/L1.2, Rw/L1.3, Wt/L1.1, Wt/L1.2, Wt/L1.3, Wt/L1.4, Wt/L1.5, Ws/L1.1, Ws/L1.2, Ws/L1.3, Ww/L1.1, Ww/L1.2

Every picture tells a story, page 89

NC

English KS3

1.1a; 2.1a, e, f, g, h, i; 2.3a, w; 3.1b, e; 3.3d, e; 4.1b, c, e

English KS4

1.1a; 2.1b, c, f, h, i, j; 2.3b, o; 3.1b, d; 3.3c, e; 4.1b, c

PSHE Personal wellbeing KS3

2.1e; 2.3c; 4c, e

PSHE Personal wellbeing KS4

2.1d; 2.3c; 4d, f

Adult Core Curriculum

SLlr/L1.1, SLlr/L1.2, SLlr/L1.3, SLlr/L1.4, SLlr/L1.5, SLlr/L1.6, SLc/L1.1, SLc/L1.2, SLc/L1.3, SLc/L1.4, SLd/L1.1, SLd/L1.2, SLd/L1.3, Rw/L1.2, Rw/L1.3, Ws/L1.1, Ws/L1.2, Ws/L1.3, Ww/L1.1, Ww/L1.2

Body language 1, pages 90–93

NC

English KS3

1.1a; 2.1a, e, f, g, h, i; 2.3a, w; 3.1b, e; 3.3d, e; 4.1b, c, e

English KS4

1.1a; 2.1b, c, f, h, i, j; 2.3b, o; 3.1b, d; 3.3c, e; 4.1b, c

PSHE Personal wellbeing KS3

2.1e; 2.3c; 4c, e

PSHE Personal wellbeing KS4

2.1d; 2.3c; 4d, f

Adult Core Curriculum

SLlr/L1.1, SLlr/L1.2, SLlr/L1.3, SLlr/L1.4, SLlr/L1.5, SLlr/L1.6, SLc/L1.1, SLc/L1.2, SLc/L1.3, SLc/L1.4, SLd/L1.1, SLd/L1.2, SLd/L1.3, Rw/L1.2, Rw/L1.3, Ws/L1.1, Ws/L1.2, Ws/L1.3, Ww/L1.1, Ww/L1.2

Mapping

Body language 2, pages 94–97

NC

English KS3

1.1a; 2.1a, e, f, g, h, i; 2.3a, w; 3.1b, e; 3.3d, e; 4.1b, c, e

English KS4

1.1a; 2.1b, c, f, h, i, j; 2.3b, o; 3.1b, d; 3.3c, e; 4.1b, c

PSHE Personal wellbeing KS3

2.1e; 2.3c; 4c, e

PSHE Personal wellbeing KS4

2.1d; 2.3c; 4d, f

Adult Core Curriculum

SLlr/L1.1, SLlr/L1.2, SLlr/L1.3, SLlr/L1.4, SLlr/L1.5, SLlr/L1.6, SLc/L1.1, SLc/L1.2, SLc/L1.3, SLc/L1.4, SLd/L1.1, SLd/L1.2, SLd/L1.3, Rw/L1.2, Rw/L1.3, Ws/L1.1, Ws/L1.2, Ws/L1.3, Ww/L1.1, Ww/L1.2

Stranded, pages 98–100

NC

English KS3

1.1a, b, c, e; 2.1a, b, e, f, g, h, i; 2.2a; 2.3a, b, e, g, h, k, p, q, s, t, u, v, w; 3.1b, e; 3.3a, c, d, e; 3.4a; 4.1b, c, e

English KS4

1.1a, c, d, e; 2.1a, b, c, f, h, i, j; 2.2a; 2.3a, b, d, e, f, g, l, m, n, o; 3.1b, d; 3.3a, c, e; 3.4d; 4.1b, c, d

PSHE Personal wellbeing KS3

2.3c; 4c, e

PSHE Personal wellbeing KS4

2.3c; 4d, f

Adult Core Curriculum

SLlr/L1.1, SLlr/L1.2, SLlr/L1.3, SLlr/L1.4, SLlr/L1.5, SLlr/L1.6, SLc/L1.1, SLc/L1.2, SLc/L1.3, SLc/L1.4, SLd/L1.1, SLd/L1.2, SLd/L1.3, Rw/L1.2, Rw/L1.3, Wt/L1.1, Wt/L1.2, Wt/L1.3, Wt/L1.4, Wt/L1.5, Wt/L1.6, Ws/L1.1, Ws/L1.2, Ws/L1.3, Ww/L1.1, Ww/L1.2